Penguin  Readers

Penguin Readers

VIRUSES AND PANDEMICS

ROS WRIGHT

LEVEL

ILLUSTRATED BY GUY HARVEY
SERIES EDITOR: SORREL PITTS

PENGUIN BOOKS

UK | USA | Canada | Ireland | Australia
India | New Zealand | South Africa

Penguin Books is part of the Penguin Random House group of companies
whose addresses can be found at global.penguinrandomhouse.com.
www.penguin.co.uk www.puffin.co.uk www.ladybird.co.uk

First published by Penguin Books Ltd, 2021
001

Text written by Ros Wright
Text copyright © Penguin Books Ltd, 2021
Illustrations copyright © Guy Harvey 2021
Cover image copyright © Ustyna Shevchuk/Shutterstock

Photo credits
p13 top © GraphicsRF.com/Shutterstock, bottom © SkyPics Studio/Shutterstock;
p22 © airdone/Shutterstock; p24 left © RHJPhtotoandilustration/Shutterstock, centre © Broccoli Photography/
Alamy Stock Photo, right © 9Gawin/Shutterstock; p37 © Maks Narodenko/Shutterstock; p39 © Leah-Anne
Thompson/Shutterstock; p42 © Everett Collection/Shutterstock; p51 © Asanka Ratnayake/LNP/Shutterstock;
p52 © The Aurum Institute; p53 © Norman James/Toronto Star via Getty Images; p59 © Everett Collection/
Shutterstock; p70 © NEOC Pakistan/A. Zaidi; p76 © The National Archives/SSPL/Getty Images;
p77 top © Eric Johnson Photography/Shutterstock, inset © UK Government; p81 © Chronicle of World History/
Alamy Stock Photo; p84 © ITV/Shutterstock; p85 © Dan Loh/AP/Shutterstock; p90 © Bettmann/Getty Images

Printed in Hong Kong

The authorized representative in the EEA is Penguin Random House Ireland,
Morrison Chambers, 32 Nassau Street, Dublin D02 YH68.

A CIP catalogue record for this book is available from the British Library

ISBN: 978-0-241-49316-8

All correspondence to:
Penguin Books
Penguin Random House Children's
One Embassy Gardens, 8 Viaduct Gardens,
London SW11 7BW

Contents

Note about the book

This book is about viruses and was written during the COVID-19 **pandemic*** of 2020. First, you will learn about the difference between **bacteria** and viruses, as well as how a virus develops and **spreads**. Then you will learn about different viruses, including their **symptoms** and how to treat them – from the **common** cold and flu to smallpox and polio, to Ebola and the Zika virus. You will also meet some of the scientists who discovered ways to prevent these diseases, as well as those who work with viruses today.

Later you will go on a journey to learn about some of the most important pandemics through history, the Black Death, the Spanish flu and HIV/AIDS. This book will also consider the ways **governments** and international **organizations** try to manage these viruses and stop future pandemics.

Viruses enter our lives in many different ways, including through language and within areas of **culture**. We see the power of language and how it is used as a tool. And we also see how artists, singers, authors and dancers have helped to record viruses through their art.

You will read about the **survivors** of viruses, including one of the oldest survivors of the Spanish flu. Finally, we look towards the future and the aims of the United Nations (UN) as it tries to prevent and treat other viruses by 2030.

*Definitions of words in **bold** can be found in the glossary on pages 103–110.

Before-reading questions

1 Have you ever had a cold or flu? Describe what it was like.

2 Which of these diseases are caused by viruses, do you think?

   a Chickenpox   **e** Measles

   b COVID-19   **f** The plague

   c Influenza   **g** Polio

   d Malaria   **h** Tuberculosis

3 What different jobs will be discussed in this book, do you think?

4 What is a pandemic? What do you already know about them?

5 Why is it important to learn about viruses and pandemics, do you think?

Body parts and symptoms

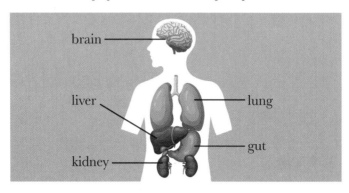

  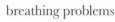

blocked nose   breathing problems   chills

cough   diarrhoea   dizziness

lump   nausea   rash

runny nose   sneeze   swollen gland   vomiting

CHAPTER ONE

An introduction to microbiology

To understand viruses, first, it is important to understand what they are, where they come from and what they can do. Welcome to the very *very* small world of microbiology – the study of microorganisms.

Microbes

Micro means "small" in Greek and *microbes* are the smallest kind of life. They are so small we are not able to see most of them with the **human** eye. But, although we can't see them, we know that microbes are everywhere. They are in the water we drink, in the food we eat, in our homes and at work, on our pets and on everything we touch. The human body itself is covered in billions and billions of microbes, living on our skin, in our gut (or stomach), up our noses and in our eyes. There are lots of different types of microbe and many play an important part in keeping us healthy.

The most well-known microbes are **bacteria**. In humans, most bacteria live in the gut where they help with the food we eat and fight **infection**. Some are used to produce foods like yoghurt, blue cheese or beer.

Germs, or pathogens as they are called in the **medical** world, are microbes that cause infection. There are several types of pathogen. Some cause diseases like athlete's foot, while another is carried by **mosquitos** and causes malaria. Some bacteria are also pathogens. These pathogens cause sore throats, as well as more serious diseases like pneumonia.

The smallest microbe is the virus, which comes in different shapes and sizes. These microbes are very small. Scientists tell us that some viruses are about 10,000 times smaller than a piece of salt. Viruses are also pathogens and cause infections like the **common** cold. They also cause chickenpox and measles, as well as more dangerous diseases, like AIDS (Acquired Immunodeficiency Syndrome), SARS (Severe Acute Respiratory Syndrome) and COVID-19.

Explaining viruses

Some types of microbes, like bacteria, can live on their own. However, viruses can only live if they enter the living **cells** of humans, plants, animals or bacteria. We call this the "host" cell. Each virus carries its own nucleic acid – **DNA** or RNA – and **protein** and has a special spiky coat to protect it. This special coat helps the virus to join the host cell. Next, DNA or RNA from the virus enters the host cell. Once it is inside the host cell, the virus's DNA or RNA begins to control the cell. First, it destroys the DNA of the host cell and then starts to produce new viruses. Finally, the host cell opens up, and the new viruses escape. Each new virus then enters a new host cell and the story begins again as the number of viruses continues to grow and **spread** through the body.

Types of virus

Adenovirus

Bacteriophage

COVID-19

Ebola Virus

Hepatitis B

Herpes Virus

HIV

Influenza

Papillomavirus

Rabies Virus

Rotavirus

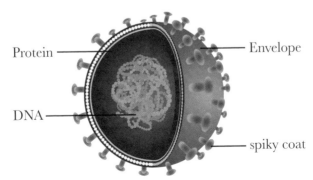

Protein — Envelope

DNA — spiky coat

Parts of a virus

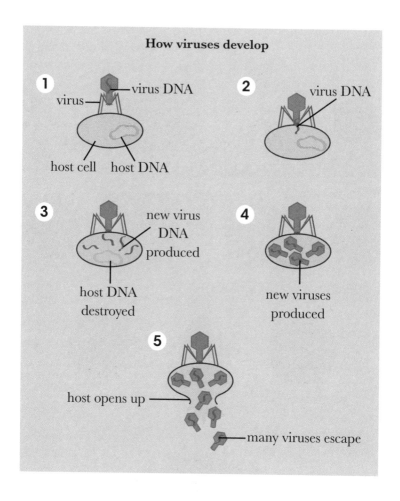

Transmitting viruses

So how do viruses enter the body? And how are they **transmitted**? Viruses can live for some time on our clothes, on a door handle or on a coin. So, one way to transmit this microbe is by touching something that already has a virus on it and then touching the face. According to **research** we touch our face around sixteen times an hour and young children probably more often. But viruses can also be transmitted through the mouth and nose by breathing them in, or through broken skin after a cut or an insect bite when the virus gets into the blood.

Another way to transmit viruses like a cold, influenza or chickenpox to another person is through the air by sneezing, coughing or simply by talking. In 2019, scientists at the University of Bristol in the UK discovered that the 100,000 pathogens from one sneeze could travel up to 160 kilometres an hour. This can **infect** another person two metres away, usually in the first few minutes. Other ways to transmit viruses between humans are during unprotected sex or by kissing. A mother might also transmit a virus to her baby. This can happen before or during the birth, or after, through the mother's milk.

Herpes simplex virus-1 (HSV-1), also called herpes, is the virus that causes cold sores – a small painful area on or around the lips. Herpes can be transmitted quite easily from person to person by touching the skin, kissing or sharing food. It can also be transmitted by drinking from the same glass or using the same towel.

Viruses can be transmitted in water. This happens very often in countries where water is not safe to drink. We can also find viruses in food, for example meat and fish. People working in hotel kitchens or in factories where food is produced must be very careful and wash their hands often, otherwise they could easily transmit viruses through the food they prepare.

Many of the viruses we know actually come from animals or insects. Birds and insects carry viruses across land, or from country to country, without ever becoming ill themselves. These viruses are then transmitted to humans or other animals. Humans can become infected with some viruses after touching the urine or faeces of infected animals or by eating infected meat. Sometimes viruses even jump from birds or animals like **bats** to humans, to create a new type of virus. Rabies can be transmitted to humans from dogs and the hantavirus from rats. Many of these viruses cause very dangerous diseases that can kill humans, for example, the SARS virus.

Plants also carry viruses. The tobacco mosaic virus (TMV), for example, infects the leaves we use to make cigarettes. TMV can also infect other types of plant, including vegetables. When the disease appears in tomatoes, it damages them, and the only way to stop it is to destroy all the infected plants. This can result in farms losing extremely large amounts of money.

However, infection does not always cause disease. People can become infected and carry a virus without actually becoming ill. These people are called carriers. Disease only happens if the infection damages the cells in the body. This means viruses may only cause disease in some people, while many more can just be carriers. Viruses also act in different ways. Some viruses affect cats but not dogs, for example, and a virus that infects a dog may not infect a human; one example of this is parvovirus.

Incubation and contagious periods

The time after catching the virus but before the **symptoms** appear is called the incubation period. During this time, the virus is developing. Each virus has its own incubation period.

The incubation period for influenza is just one to four days and for chickenpox it is between fourteen to sixteen days. For a virus like HIV it is two to six weeks. Incubation periods can also be different for different people because of their age, their general health and their **immune system**. The **contagious** period is the time when another person can catch the disease from you, or you can catch it from someone else. The contagious period is also different with each virus. It usually starts when a person has symptoms, but it can sometimes start during the incubation period when you still have no symptoms.

Fighting viruses

The human body has its own ways of fighting viruses. Hairs in the nose and mucus (thick **liquid**) in the nose, mouth and throat all try to stop microbes entering the body. They are then pushed out through a sneeze, cough or in faeces or urine. If this doesn't work, the immune system tries to help.

White blood cells are a very important part of the body's immune system. They live in different parts of the body, including in the neck, in the gut, in the nose and in the throat. When new proteins appear in a human cell, the immune system learns that a new virus has entered the body. When this happens, the white blood cell develops a new kind of cell that creates proteins called **antibodies**. The job of the antibodies is to fight against the virus and stop it from spreading. When a patient has a high temperature, headache, swollen (large) glands (in the neck) or a rash (on the skin), it means their immune system is working hard to kill the virus. The first time the immune system meets a new virus it may take some time to destroy it. The next time the same virus appears, the antibodies in the immune system remember it and destroy it. This means you get better much faster. However, if the patient is no longer **immune**, they can become infected again.

Some viruses, like flu viruses for example, don't disappear. Instead they change and develop into something new. Then, how much they spread depends on the environment. They will spread more easily in environments where there are larger numbers of people living or gathering in small, closed spaces.

Good viruses

Finally, it is important to say that not all viruses are bad. Some viruses work as part of the immune system to infect and kill bacteria. Some even kill other viruses. These "good" viruses can be found in the gut, in blood and in the skin. In 2014, scientists at the New York University Langone Medical Center in America did studies on mice which showed that a virus could fight and kill infection in the gut. They believe the same is possible for humans. Other new studies show some viruses can even help to fight and kill **cancer** cells.

Scientists studying this area of microbiology discover new information about "good" viruses every day. They hope this information will help them to better understand infections. They also hope to learn new ideas about how to stop serious viruses and diseases spreading in the future.

CHAPTER TWO

Common viruses and childhood diseases

Viruses are with us all the time, although some more often than others. These viruses can be put into two different groups: common viruses, like a cold or a sore throat, and what we call **childhood** diseases. Childhood diseases are illnesses like chickenpox, which are usually, but not always, caught when we are very young.

The common cold

We often talk about the "common cold". Common, because there are hundreds of different cold viruses. In fact, the cold is so common that a five-year-old might get six or seven a year, and sometimes as many as twelve. The main reason for this is that children spend a lot of time together in quite small spaces, like school classrooms, where viruses spread extremely quickly. According to the Centers for Disease Control and Prevention (CDC), American children miss twenty-two million days of school a year because of the common cold. Women between twenty and thirty get more colds than men; this may be because they are more likely to either look after or work with small children. But as we get older, we catch fewer colds because we have developed **immunity** to more cold viruses. Most sixty-year-olds will probably only have one cold a year. Another point is that young children often share toys that they have put in their mouths, and they don't wash their hands as often as adults, so they spread germs more easily. Most colds – there could be 200 different cold viruses at any one time – are more common in the winter months. This is not only because cold viruses prefer lower temperatures, but also because we spend more time inside, which makes it easier to spread the virus to other members of the family.

Most cold viruses, called rhinoviruses, start in and around the nose and symptoms are well-known. They usually start with a runny nose and lots of coughing and sneezing. Later, when it becomes more difficult to breathe, the person suffering may get a sore throat.

Scientists and **pharmaceutical** companies across the world have spent a lot of time and money trying to find a **cure** for the common cold, but they have not been successful yet. In order to treat a cold, patients are advised to drink lots of water, take lots of rest and use painkillers (pills that stop the pain). Usually you don't need to visit the doctor when you have a cold and you can buy the **medication** you need at the **pharmacy** or even the supermarket, although this depends on the country. The mistake that some people make is to ask their doctor for antibiotics when they have a cold. Sadly, these never work on the common cold as antibiotics are only used for treating illnesses caused by bacteria.

Influenza

Many people confuse having a cold with influenza, or "the flu" as it is usually known. So how do you know if you have the flu or just a common cold? While a cold develops slowly, the flu will hit you immediately. If you have a cold, you can usually continue working or going to school as the symptoms are quite **mild**. But anyone with the flu is unlikely to have enough energy and may need to sleep for a few days until the symptoms stop. Like patients with a cold, flu patients may also have a cough. Often the difference is the type of cough: a dry cough for the person with flu and a mucus cough for someone with a cold. Patients with the flu will have a **fever**, which means their temperature will be above 38°C. It is likely they will also have backache and a headache and will probably not feel very hungry. Some may also experience nausea (feeling sick) and vomiting (being sick).

There are three groups of flu virus. Influenza C viruses produce quite mild symptoms and Influenza B viruses have stronger symptoms. Influenza A is the strongest group of flu viruses; these can infect not only humans but also pigs, horses and even dolphins. It is an extremely contagious virus, which usually appears in young children before transferring to adults. A healthy person can transmit the flu virus a day before they have symptoms. So, it is possible to pass on the flu before you know you have it and then continue to transmit the virus for up to five to seven days after the symptoms appear.

For a few people, the flu can develop into a more serious illness like pneumonia. Unlike many other diseases, pneumonia can either come from a virus or from bacteria. Both types are serious illnesses that stop the lungs working correctly and can sometimes even cause death. There are also **complications** for **pregnant** women who catch flu. Their babies can be born too early or with a low birth weight. Sadly, in more serious situations, these babies can even die before birth.

Childhood diseases

Childhood diseases are illnesses that are often caught by young children. In fact, it is possible that most of us have had at least one of these diseases before the age of ten. While adults can catch these illnesses, it is better to catch them as a child because the symptoms are not as bad and there are fewer complications. Chickenpox, mumps, measles and rubella or German measles are possibly the most well-known childhood diseases caused by viruses.

Mumps is very common in young children, but it is not usually dangerous. The most obvious symptom of mumps is the area around the neck, just below the ears, that is swollen. This makes it difficult to eat and drink. Later the patient may feel tired and have a high temperature. Mumps can be treated quite easily by having lots of rest, drinking plenty of water and eating food that is soft and easy to eat. This could be soup, eggs, yoghurt or cooked apple. Patients can take painkillers to bring their fever down and can usually return to work or school after a week.

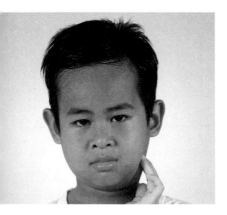

Child with mumps

Chickenpox, measles and German measles all come from viruses that attack the immune

20

system. Chickenpox is caused by the *varicella-zoster virus*, measles by the *rubeola virus*, and German measles, the *rubella virus*. All of them are highly contagious and can be caught when an infected person sneezes or coughs. The incubation period for measles is between one and two weeks before becoming infected. It is a little longer for chickenpox, between two and three weeks, and around seventeen days for German measles. People who have German measles are most contagious from the week before the rash appears until about one week after the rash goes away. With measles, the virus is most contagious from four days before, until four days after the rash first appears. For chickenpox someone is contagious two days before the spots appear and until the scabs appear.

There is no cure for any of these childhood diseases and the best advice is to take lots of rest, keep drinking water and take paracetamol – a type of painkiller – to stop any fever. And for chickenpox, parents are advised to give children special medication or to put special cream on the skin to stop them from scratching the blisters.

Childhood diseases: a case study

As the symptoms for several childhood diseases are similar, let's compare three eight-year-olds, Lucas, Anwar and Mia, so we can see the differences. All three of them are feeling unwell and have a rash, but each rash is different. For Lucas, red spots started to appear on his chest, face and back and then spread all over his body. The spots filled with an infected liquid called pus that turned into blisters. Lucas is trying not to scratch the

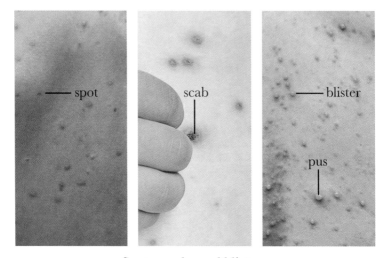

Spots, scabs and blisters

blisters to stop them from spreading, but like most children he is finding this really difficult. Some of the blisters have already dried and become scabs. The thing Mia noticed first was some white spots in her mouth. Then came a red-brown rash that appeared on her forehead, which later spread down her face and neck and on to her body and legs. Her spots are now beginning to join together but there are no blisters and she doesn't try to scratch the skin. Unlike Lucas, Mia also has a sore throat, a runny nose and red, watery eyes. Both children have a fever, but while Mia still wants to eat her food, Lucas is no longer hungry. Anwar's symptoms are very similar to Mia's. He has a pink or red rash that started on his face and then spread to the rest of his body. Anwar also has a mild fever and is suffering from a runny nose and red, watery eyes. However, unlike Mia, Anwar has also noticed his neck and throat have swollen.

Getting the **diagnosis** right is not easy. The nurse at Lucas's school announced an **outbreak** of chickenpox the week before so his parents knew that was what he had. However, neither Anwar nor Mia's parents were sure what their children were suffering from. Anwar's doctor asked him to do a blood test so that he could make the right diagnosis. It was German measles. Mia's doctor **diagnosed** measles and told her to stay at home for three weeks. Lucas and Anwar would probably be back at school after a week or ten days.

Complications

For an adult who catches chickenpox there can be complications. If an adult has chickenpox for the first time, the symptoms are the same as for children but worse. It's not unusual to have 500 blisters on the skin. But, as with many diseases, complications are more common if patients already have other conditions, such as HIV or cancer, or if they take some types of medication.

There are complications with chickenpox or German measles if a woman is pregnant. Before her baby is born it can catch the disease through the mother's blood. These diseases can stop the baby from growing correctly, stop its ability to hear, as well as cause problems for the baby's heart and brain. So, where possible, it is important for a woman to get a **vaccine** a month before trying to have a baby, unless she was **vaccinated** as a child.

Often if the patient is older, for example fifty years or more, and has already had chickenpox, they might develop another disease called shingles. Shingles comes from the same virus as chickenpox, which can "sleep" for many years before it suddenly appears again. It can then appear again and again several times over. Symptoms include red spots in the same place on just one side of the body. These fill with pus and join together, before turning into blisters. The patient may also have a fever and headaches. Shingles usually lasts for two to three weeks but is only contagious if someone touches the pus of an infected person. There are many complications of shingles, some of which are quite dangerous. However, it is now possible to treat shingles with special medicine called an antiviral.

Man flu

Finally, a few words about "man flu". For many years there has been a discussion about how men and women experience the common cold. Some men say they experience stronger cold symptoms than women. Earlier research had **suggested** that male animals in general have weaker immune systems. But is this also true for humans? In 2010, a new research study at Cambridge University in the UK investigated the possible differences between male and female patients and their colds. The results of the research are interesting but don't prove anything for the moment. For now, "man flu" remains just a story in the media.

CHAPTER THREE

Serious viruses

It is often said that there are ten times more viruses in the world than there are stars in the sky. In fact, it is almost impossible to know how many viruses there are at any one time. The ones included in this chapter are some of the most serious viruses we know about. Some are thought to be extremely dangerous, but luckily others have either disappeared or almost disappeared.

Norovirus

If you travel on long journeys by sea, then one virus you may have heard of is norovirus. Norovirus doesn't only appear on expensive holiday ships, but it can develop where there are lots of people living or working very closely together in a small space. This might include young children at school, patients in hospital or those in special homes for older people. This virus is also called the "winter sickness bug". Like the flu, it is highly contagious, often affecting pregnant women and older people with poor immune systems.

It is necessary to try and protect ourselves from this type of infection by avoiding infected food and water. Of course, this is difficult if you are in a hotel, on a ship or in a hospital as you are not able to prepare your own food. In one example, norovirus attacked 333 people across thirteen states in the US. The outbreak was connected to workers preparing food for a company selling cars in different parts of the country.

Once someone has become infected with the virus, they usually suffer stomach pain followed by vomiting and diarrhoea. Some may also experience a fever and muscle pain. The symptoms can be quite strong, but most people will only experience these symptoms for two or three days and then get better. There is no treatment for norovirus and patients are asked to stay at home, rest and drink lots of water.

Although norovirus doesn't usually last for very long, the faeces of the patient can continue to contain the virus for several more weeks. This is good to know when you are looking after an infected person and are responsible for washing and cleaning them and their clothes. In fact, this virus is extremely difficult to kill. Not only can it continue to live even in very hot temperatures – up to 60°C – it also stays alive after cleaning infected areas with very strong cleaning liquids. It is also very easy to become infected again. The virus itself is always changing and so patients who have had norovirus are not always protected the next time there is an outbreak.

For some, the symptoms can be more serious, and it is reported that there are about 50,000 child deaths a year from norovirus. If someone becomes **dehydrated** because they are unable to drink enough water, for example, or they cough blood, then they must see a doctor immediately. Sadly, the result of a serious norovirus infection where the person is finally unable to eat or drink is death.

Scientists have discovered that some people are more likely to catch norovirus than others. In fact, there is a connection with blood type. Scientists have found that people with blood type B were less likely to catch some types of norovirus than people from other blood groups. According to research, this means that around one third of the passengers on a ship will not catch norovirus if there is an outbreak while they are travelling.

Smallpox

While we could very easily meet norovirus today, it is more or less impossible to meet smallpox. This virus was around for centuries, and there have been examples of it in many countries across the world. Pictures of the Egyptian Pharaoh Rameses V, who died in 1145 BCE, showed that he probably had smallpox. Around 30% of those who caught smallpox would die, with two million people dying from the disease in 1967 alone. After a huge international **vaccination programme** the last person to catch smallpox was in Somalia in 1977, and in 1980 the World Health **Organization** (WHO) announced the virus was destroyed. Today, the smallpox virus can only be found in **laboratories**.

People who catch smallpox, which is caused by the variola virus and is similar to measles, experience several symptoms. These begin, like flu viruses, with a fever and being extremely tired, back pain and a headache and in some cases vomiting. Usually the patient is not contagious during this time, but they are often too ill to work or go to school. In the days that follow, red spots appear, first on the tongue, then on the face, hands and arms and later on the body. Although the patient may look worse at this moment, they actually start to feel better.

The spots then fill with pus and the fever returns. This is the moment when the patient is most contagious. As the pus begins to dry and become scabs, the patient is still contagious. The scabs finally fall off and leave very small holes in the skin. This is something that you might notice on the face of someone who has had smallpox.

Polio

Polio is another disease that today we can say has almost disappeared thanks to **vaccination**. However, it is yet another virus without a cure. The polio virus causes an infection in the bowel and can be transmitted by sneezing and coughing, in faeces or through unclean water or infected food. In the 20th century parents feared this disease because it affected thousands of children, mostly under the age of five. In the UK during the early 1950s, 8,000 children a year lost the use of their legs because of polio.

In most cases people who catch polio won't experience any symptoms and their body will be able to fight the infection. In fact, they may not even know they have been infected, although of course they could still infect someone else. Most children who experience symptoms will be ill for about a week and suffer from a fever, sore throat, headache, stomach ache and muscle pain, nausea and vomiting. For a few children however, symptoms are much worse. The virus attacks the **nervous system** in the back and the area near the brain. This can cause paralysis, usually in the legs, which means you can't move them, and it becomes almost impossible to walk. For some people the virus can cause muscles to become weak and it can also stop the muscles in the feet and legs from developing correctly. Another serious symptom is that it becomes extremely difficult for the patient to breathe, which can kill them. These problems may only last for a short time for some patients, but for others they could last their whole life.

It is necessary to treat polio patients in hospital with painkillers and rest. Patients may also need to spend some time on a ventilator, a machine to help them breathe. This must be followed by lots of exercise to avoid problems in the legs and feet and training to help them walk again.

Ebola

A different kind of virus is Ebola, a disease first transmitted to humans from animals. A recent outbreak started in late 2013 in Guinea and then moved to Sierra Leone and Liberia in early 2014. During this outbreak, more than 28,600 people were infected and 11,325 people died. Women were generally the worst affected. In Liberia, it is thought around 75% of the people who died were women. The first time the virus appeared was in 1976, in two countries at the same time: South Sudan and the Democratic Republic of the Congo. In June 2020 it was announced that the Democratic Republic of the Congo had **identified** new cases of Ebola.

The Ebola virus probably first came from fruit bats but has since been transmitted to humans through the blood or urine of infected animals. Eating what is called "bushmeat" – the meat of wild animals like monkeys – is another way to transmit the virus from the animal world to humans. The virus then spreads between humans in the same way, through blood, urine, faeces or by vomiting. It can also be transmitted through unprotected sex, and mothers can give it to their new baby either before they are born or after when feeding. Ebola is extremely contagious and can continue living for several days outside of the body. In fact, it is so contagious it can even be spread simply by touching the body of someone who is either infected or has died from the virus.

Ebola begins with a list of well-known symptoms, including fever, muscle pain, headaches and a sore throat. Then diarrhoea, vomiting and a rash can be added to the list. As the infection continues the situation becomes more serious, however, as the patient's liver and kidneys stop working and they experience bleeding from the ears, eyes, nose and mouth.

For the moment there is no cure or any way to stop people catching the Ebola virus, although these are being developed and tested. The only way to manage the disease is to **quarantine** patients and treat them in hospital rooms where they are alone. Sadly, at the moment, one in two patients with Ebola will die.

SARS

Like Ebola, SARS-CoV (severe acute respiratory syndrome coronavirus) is transmitted to humans from animals, possibly in animal markets where the virus changes and then jumps from animals to humans. Although scientists are still not sure which animal actually carries the virus and transmits it to humans, they believe it is bats. Like Ebola, there is no cure for SARS and scientists are trying to develop a way to stop people from catching it.

The SARS virus was first discovered in humans in 2002 in an area of South China. It quickly spread to twenty-six other countries, mostly in Asia, but also in Europe, Australia and North America. During this time, the virus infected just over 8,000 people and there were 774 deaths.

SARS is spread in the same way as a cold or flu virus: person-to-person. So, it is important to stay away from infected people and take care to cover your mouth when sneezing or coughing and wash your hands as often as possible. The symptoms are similar to those for the flu, and appear up to a week after being close to an infected person. But then after this, the lungs become infected, and the patient finds it more and more difficult to breathe. The only way to treat someone with SARS is to quarantine them in hospital, treat them with medication and put them on a ventilator to help them breathe.

Possibly what worries **governments** the most about SARS is how it is transmitted. Not all cases of SARS have been transmitted from animal to human. In 2004, the Chinese government announced another outbreak of the virus. This time it was connected to the National Institute of the Virology Laboratory in Beijing where two of the nine who caught the disease were students testing the SARS virus. The other seven people were connected to the two students, including the mother of one and nurses who were treating them. Since then, neither China nor any other country has reported any new cases of SARS.

COVID-19

In December 2019, the first cases of a new coronavirus, COVID-19, were discovered in the Wuhan Province of China. By July 2020, more than fifty countries in the world had cases of this new virus and hundreds of thousands had already died.

COVID-19 is transmitted in the same way as influenza and symptoms of the disease are also very similar. These symptoms appear between two and fourteen days after contact with an infected person and are usually a fever, dry cough, muscle pain, headaches and breathing problems. Other symptoms have been discovered which are different, like not being able to taste and smell food, while many people don't suffer any symptoms at all.

What is very different is the way the virus affects some people. For most their symptoms will be mild. In the case of patients who are older, have **diabetes**, asthma, heart problems or are overweight their situation can become extremely dangerous and, in some cases, they will die.

CHAPTER FOUR

Treatment and prevention

There are often no cures for viruses and so we have to find other ways to control them and stop them from spreading. We can usually treat the symptoms and prevent them spreading further, sometimes very simply and cheaply.

Treatment

The important thing to understand when we talk about treatment is that it is extremely difficult to treat viral infections. There are several reasons for this. First of all, there are so many of them. Also, unlike bacteria, viruses cannot **survive** alone – they "hide" inside a host cell and it is difficult to find them without destroying the host cell – and they are not connected to each other. Different viruses also have different nucleic acid – DNA or RNA – and some have very different shapes and are always changing or mutating. So, while it is possible to use the same medication for different bacterial infections, a new **drug** is usually needed to treat each new virus.

We generally treat the symptoms, like headaches, rashes and vomiting, but not the virus itself. Doctors will **prescribe** a cream for the rashes to stop a patient from scratching, medicine for a sore throat, something to stop a runny nose or painkillers to bring down a fever. There are medications that can stop us from feeling sick and vomiting and tablets that will stop diarrhoea. However, parents need to be careful as some of the treatments cannot be given to babies and very young children. Doctors will advise patients to drink lots of water to avoid **dehydration** and drink soup and have plenty of rest to help build their immune system. If the symptoms are mild, the patient may not even need any treatment.

It is now possible to treat some viruses with what we call antiviral drugs, but not many. An antiviral drug is a medicine that stops the virus from developing in the body. Some even prevent the virus entering the host cell. If a patient has a virus and a bacterial infection at the same time, they may need to take antivirals and antibiotics.

Antiviral drugs can be used for different kinds of virus. For skin infections, like herpes for example, antiviral cream can treat the blisters that appear. Medication can also cut the number and length of outbreaks of the virus. Oseltamivir, a popular antiviral drug, is prescribed across the world to treat the symptoms of the flu. It is also given to patients with a weak immune system to prevent them catching the virus. People who take this medication may experience **side effects**, like nausea and vomiting, and a few may notice an **allergy**, a rash, breathing problems or dizziness, although this is very unusual. Unlike antibiotics used to treat bacterial infections, antiviral drugs can only be used to treat one kind of virus. However, after some time, just like antibiotics, viruses finally get used to antiviral drugs, and they can stop working.

Of course, there are other ways that people use to treat the symptoms of a mild virus like the common cold, although they are not all medical. In fact, many countries have their own special ways of treating cold symptoms like a sore throat or a blocked nose. Eating garlic or drinking garlic tea is a common way to treat a cold in Morocco, Spain and countries in Latin America. But studies have shown it is probably better to eat it before getting a cold and not after it has begun. Honey is very popular for a sore throat. According to research, a spoon of honey at night will help stop coughing and help the patient to sleep. One study of two-year-old children found that honey was just as good as some medication from the pharmacy. Across the world there are some other more unusual ways to treat cold symptoms. One of the strangest treatments that may have come from the UK is where in the past people used to put butter around the throat and then cover the neck with dirty socks. It is not clear if or how this treatment works but it certainly is very unusual.

Garlic is used to treat colds in many countries.

Preventing infection in hospital

Preventing and controlling infection is one of the most important subjects for anyone working in health. While it is impossible to prevent all viruses from spreading in hospitals, research tells us we can stop most of them. However, this is only possible if there are strict rules that everyone follows. These rules are so strict that in many countries, if hospital workers don't follow them, it becomes a problem of law.

So how do nurses and doctors help prevent infection from spreading as they work? First, they need to understand the different causes of infection – bacteria, viruses, etc. – and how they are transmitted. Then, it is important to know the symptoms of infection as well as which patients are most likely to become infected. And finally, the different ways of preventing infection.

We know there are groups of patients with weaker immune systems who are more likely to catch infections in hospital than others and need to be protected. These patients include babies and young children, as well as older people and those with serious illnesses like cancer and HIV.

While everyone knows that the simplest way to prevent infection is by washing your hands, it is even more important to do it well. There are several steps to follow and these include using hot water and liquid soap, washing the ends and between the fingers and not touching the tap after you have finished washing. Washing your hands well takes longer than you think. During the COVID-19 **pandemic**, children around the world were encouraged to sing the "Happy Birthday" song twice to remind them to continue washing their hands for twenty seconds.

Health workers wear special clothes called Personal Protective **Equipment**, or PPE, when they are treating patients. PPE not only protects the patient; it also protects the health worker. PPE – plastic gloves, aprons and sometimes masks to cover the face – is used to do even the simplest job, like moving patients or giving injections. Health workers are trained to put on and take off PPE in a special way to help prevent further infection. And once they have taken off their PPE, it must be thrown away immediately.

Some viruses (and bacteria) are much more difficult to control in a hospital. Norovirus, for example, spreads extremely quickly amongst people who are already ill and living in small closed spaces. In the UK, patients who catch norovirus or MRSA (another hospital virus) are immediately moved to a room by themselves with their own bathroom to protect other patients. We call this isolation. As soon as the patient is better, the room

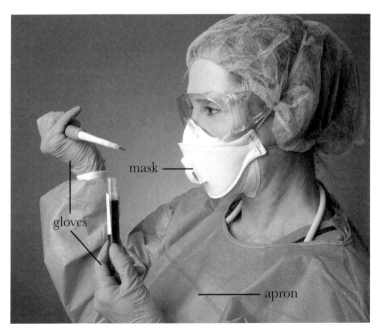

mask

gloves

apron

Health worker in PPE

must be cleaned from top to bottom before it can be used again.

It is important to educate patients and visitors and to help them understand how infections are transmitted. Nurses advise patients and relatives how to prevent infection at home so that the patient can continue to be safe after they leave hospital. Family and friends are asked not to visit patients if they themselves are ill with flu symptoms, diarrhoea, vomiting or rashes. They should also avoid bringing young children and babies into a hospital as it may not be safe for them or the patients. Visitors should always wash their hands before they enter the patient's room and after they leave. They should not touch any medical equipment or sit on the patient's bed. Hospitals and doctor's offices will always have information about infection control for patients and their visitors to read. It is important everyone works together to be sure we don't spread disease and infection while in a hospital.

Vaccination

In medicine, one of the greatest moments of the 20th century was when it was announced that smallpox had disappeared in almost every country in the world. The reason for this was a new **technique** called vaccination. Vaccination is the best way of preventing a virus from spreading.

A vaccine is a type of medication that trains the immune system to recognize a virus and create antibodies to fight against it. Unlike medication that you take after catching a virus, vaccines need to be taken before the virus arrives. When an outbreak happens, someone who is vaccinated will not usually become infected because they have the antibodies to fight the virus. If they do become infected, the symptoms will usually only be very mild. Vaccines can protect people for several years.

For many, the history of vaccination begins with Edward Jenner in 1796 and the development of a vaccine for smallpox. However, an earlier type of vaccination used to protect against smallpox, called *variolation*, was used in China in the 16th century. The Chinese injected the pus from smallpox spots under the skin of people not yet infected by the virus. The idea behind this technique was to try to protect them and stop them catching the virus, although they didn't really know why it worked. This technique was brought to England in the 1700s and was tested on prisoners at first. However, they found it was not 100% safe as people still caught smallpox, and some died, causing an **epidemic**.

Later that same century, Edward Jenner, an English doctor, was working on a different technique. He noticed that women working with cows on farms often caught cowpox – a similar but less dangerous type of virus. He also noticed that during a smallpox outbreak these farm workers didn't catch the virus. We now know their immune system was probably protecting them.

So, Jenner began developing his own technique. He put cowpox pus from an infected woman into a cut in the arm of an eight-year-old boy, James Phipps. Some weeks later, Jenner cut the boy's arm again and this time put very, very small amounts of smallpox pus into the cut. Several days later, Jenner announced his experiment had worked; James had not caught the smallpox virus. Jenner experimented on others until he was able to prove

Edward Jenner (1749–1823) injecting
James Phipps with cowpox

that his technique – vaccination – was a success and that it was also much safer than *variolation*.

Soon vaccination programmes for smallpox were introduced across Europe and, in the US, Thomas Jefferson started a similar programme. By 1800, 100,000 people had been vaccinated in Europe. And in 1853 a new law in the UK was introduced so that all babies had to have the smallpox vaccine. More than a century later it is no longer necessary to get vaccinated against smallpox as the virus can no longer be found, unless you work in a laboratory where they test the virus.

While Jenner knew his vaccination worked, he did not know why. One hundred years later, Louis Pasteur in France used what he already knew about microbiology to try and understand Jenner's vaccination technique. Pasteur understood for example that bacteria could cause sickness. He discovered that other microbes, smaller than bacteria – that we now know as viruses – could also cause sickness. Pasteur then used this information to develop a vaccine for rabies.

Polio, another deadly virus, killed tens of thousands of American children in the first half of the 20th century. Two scientists living in America, Jonas Salk and Albert Sabin, joined the race after the Second World War to find a vaccine to prevent this terrible disease. Earlier, another group of scientists, Enders, Weller and Robbins, had discovered a way to create a polio virus in a laboratory. Salk used their technique to develop a live virus that he then "killed" to create his vaccine. He believed a dead virus would be safer than a live one. First, he tested his vaccine on monkeys before testing it on himself and members of his family. Then he tried it on patients who had already had polio. Salk measured the number of antibodies the patients had before injecting them with the vaccine and then waited to see if they developed more antibodies. In 1954 around two million young children, called the "Polio Pioneers", were part of a large experiment to test the vaccine to be sure it was safe. The experiment was a success and it was announced that the vaccine was safe to use. A year later a vaccination programme for millions of children began in the US.

At the same time, Albert Sabin was developing his own

vaccine. Sabin used a live virus to develop his vaccine which he began testing, first on himself and his family, and then on other **researchers** and groups of prisoners. Children were given the vaccine on a piece of sugar. It was also a success and his vaccine was used in programmes around the world until the 2000s. Researchers now believe Salk's dead vaccine is safer than Sabin's live vaccine. In fact, this is the one used today to help prevent polio in the few countries where it is still possible to catch the disease.

Other vaccines were developed during the 20th century. Possibly the most well-known is the **MMR** vaccine that was developed in 1969. **MMR** is a vaccine that protects against three of the childhood diseases: mumps, measles and rubella. Children in the UK have their first **MMR** vaccination when they are a year old and the second just before they are three and a half. Another popular vaccine is the flu vaccine. At the moment, a new one has to be developed every year because the virus is always changing. However, scientists are exploring ways to develop a flu vaccine that will prevent all types of flu, called a universal vaccine.

For vaccination programmes to be a success, as many people as possible need to be vaccinated. Although vaccines often include a live virus, the amount is so small it doesn't usually cause the disease in a healthy person. Of course, because of poor general health, there are people who cannot be vaccinated. This includes pregnant women or people who have a blood disease, or HIV. If fewer than 90% of the **population** are vaccinated against measles for example, then it is possible for a virus to return. So, it is necessary for at least 95% of all children to be vaccinated every year in order to protect the whole population. It might be a little lower for diseases that are less contagious, such as polio where it is necessary to vaccinate 80–85%. Public Health England believes the measles vaccination has saved around 4,500 lives in the country since it was introduced in 1968, preventing some twenty million cases of measles.

Vaccine side effects

Vaccines do have side effects, but these are generally very mild and usually only last a few days. Side effects might include the arm around the injection becoming red and swollen, feeling a little unwell, developing a temperature, or a rash.

The MMR vaccine is produced from cells from a baby chicken. When MMR was first introduced, children with a very dangerous allergy to eggs called anaphylaxis were not given the vaccine and neither were children with skin diseases. However, research proved any danger from the MMR vaccine was extremely small and that it was actually safe for most people. There are cases of parents who have refused to vaccinate their children because of a fear of side effects. Sadly, some of these children have caught measles and become very dangerously ill. Some can no longer see or hear, while others now suffer very serious **disabilities**.

CHAPTER FIVE

Working with viruses

While many microbiology students leave university and go to work as researchers in laboratories, others might work in hospitals, international organizations, companies and schools. Not everyone working with viruses has studied microbiology and not everyone working with viruses works with patients.

Virologists

If they do decide to work in a laboratory, some microbiology students might become virologists. Virologists are researchers whose main job is to study the science behind viruses. They are interested in knowing how different viruses behave and develop. As they do their research, virologists might discover new viruses and then spend time examining ways to control them. Sometimes they even discover "good" viruses, which they test further to try to find out how they could be used to make our health better. Virologists usually work in hospitals or universities and some also teach microbiology students.

Epidemiologists

Other students might become epidemiologists. Epidemiologists study different types of disease including viruses. However, they don't just examine the science; they look at viruses from lots of different sides. Epidemiologists look at how and where outbreaks of a disease first begin and how they spread. Epidemiologists who work in hospitals give advice on how to control diseases like norovirus that possibly even began inside their own place of work.

The work of epidemiologists is also extremely important for governments and international organizations like the WHO. Their research can help these organizations understand how a disease spreads from city to city and even country to country. They inform people about new outbreaks so that governments can introduce **policies** to stop a virus from spreading. They also look at history to learn more. For example, they might examine the past to understand how a virus like measles almost disappeared. They then use that understanding and experience to try and explain why these diseases are now reappearing in some places.

In the US in 2018, only 14% of epidemiologists worked in hospitals. In fact, just over 50% work for the government, while the rest work in several different areas. Someone who is interested in animals, for example, could become a veterinary epidemiologist. The job of a veterinary epidemiologist is to understand how viruses, like avian influenza, are transmitted between animals and from animals to humans. Someone else might want to work for a company that produces medication and so become a pharmaceutical epidemiologist. And just like virologists, some epidemiologists also teach in universities.

However, unlike virologists, not all epidemiologists study medicine or microbiology at university. Epidemiologists also need to learn about people and how they behave. It is important for them to understand how groups of people transmit viruses. Mathematics is also important in order to produce information about the numbers of people who have caught a virus in the past. This information suggests how many people could catch it again in the future.

Pharmacists

Of course, there are many jobs for microbiology students in the world of medicine. The first place we often go when we show symptoms of a virus is the pharmacy to see a **pharmacist**. Pharmacists understand viruses and can advise patients on the right kind of medication for their symptoms. They also help patients understand when to take the medication, how much to take and for how long. They even give advice to doctors about new medications. In some countries, like the UK, pharmacists can now give flu vaccines.

Doctors and nurses

Family doctors and nurses work with viruses all day, every day. In fact, they probably speak to hundreds of patients every week experiencing common cold and flu symptoms. In the winter months or during an outbreak of chickenpox or measles, the number of visits to the family doctor may increase by 100% or more. The family doctor not only gives vaccines but also gives advice on how to prevent disease. They diagnose viruses and then prescribe different types of treatment. Other people who work with viruses in the world of medicine are school nurses. One of the jobs of a school nurse every year is to organize vaccination programmes for the students, so that they are protected from the latest flu viruses. It is also possible that new outbreaks of measles or chickenpox in a school are actually discovered by the school nurse.

Doctors working in a hospital might interview patients with a variety of different infections, including viruses, like HIV, norovirus or even Ebola. Their usual day might include answering questions about travel vaccinations, diagnosing and treating new patients and giving advice to other teams of doctors. Patients with an infection can become dangerously ill very quickly. It is the job of the doctor to work out the type of infection or virus, treat the patient, stop the virus spreading further and sometimes to even save their life.

Three virologists

The important work of virologists is often forgotten or misunderstood. There are a few very well-known male researchers in this area, like Louis Pasteur and Edward Jenner, but not so many famous women virologists. So, let us look at three female scientists whose work in microbiology has been key to understanding some of the most dangerous viruses we know.

Dr Françoise Barré-Sinoussi

First, Dr Françoise Barré-Sinoussi, a French researcher from Paris, who was born in 1947. As a child Barré-Sinoussi enjoyed watching animals and trying to understand how they behaved. At school she was good at science and wanted to become a doctor. She studied at the University of Paris during the 1960s but decided she didn't want to become a doctor once she understood how long and expensive it was going to be to train. Instead, Barré-Sinoussi became a virologist and went to work as a researcher at the famous Institut Pasteur in Paris.

During the 1980s the AIDS (Acquired Immunodeficiency Syndrome) epidemic happened, and researchers began trying everything to understand how the disease was transmitted. It was in 1983, just two years after AIDS was first discovered in the US, that Barré-Sinoussi found some important information that she hoped would help scientists understand AIDS much better. Together with Professor Luc Montagnier, Françoise Barré-Sinoussi discovered that AIDS was transmitted by the human immunodeficiency virus or HIV. This information was useful in helping to find the right kind of treatment for the disease.

She then travelled to Africa and saw how the disease was spreading. However, by this time the virus was not just spreading across Africa. HIV/AIDS, as it became known, was spreading extremely quickly across the US, Europe and Latin America. It was a world epidemic and thousands were dying. At first scientists thought the virus only affected women if they were drug addicts (people who find it difficult to stop taking drugs) sharing drug equipment. However, because of the research of Barré-Sinoussi and her team in 1983, scientists began to understand that women could also catch the disease through sex with infected male partners.

Barré-Sinoussi has since written more than 400 articles about viruses. Although they discovered the human immunodeficiency virus in 1983, Barré-Sinoussi and Montagnier were not recognized internationally until much later. In fact, this didn't happen until 2008 when they were given the Nobel Prize in Physiology or Medicine. Barré-Sinoussi has since won many other prizes over the years from different organizations, including the famous French prize, the *Légion d'honneur*, becoming a Grand Officer in 2013.

Today, thirty-eight million people live with HIV and there are still almost two million new infections every year. However, Barré-Sinoussi is happy to report that there are now antiviral drugs that fight against HIV. Not only can these drugs reduce the death rate by 90%, they can also help prevent new infections. These are drugs that patients have to take for the rest of their lives. Sadly, the story is not always so positive, and Barré-Sinoussi believes there is much work still to be done. According to Barré-Sinoussi, only 40% of patients in poorer countries are being treated and patients continue to be diagnosed late. Fear and little understanding mean that there are many people who are still very **negative** towards AIDS patients, and that people with HIV/AIDS feel unhappy talking about

Françoise Barré-Sinoussi
(1947–present)

49

their illness. But Barré-Sinoussi still has hope and feels a cure might be possible one day in the future.

Professor Gita Ramjee

Professor Gita Ramjee was also a virologist. Like Barré-Sinoussi, she was known for her research into HIV and was very interested in trying to prevent women catching the disease. Until her death in 2020, Gita worked at the South African Medical Research Council, but she also had other important jobs with several universities across the world.

Ramjee was born in Kampala, Uganda, a country her family had to leave when she was still very young. Ramjee's family moved to the UK where she studied sciences at the University

of Sunderland. As an adult she moved to South Africa and it was at the University of KwaZulu-Natal (UKZN) in Durban where she got her PhD. She was very interested in women's health and began working with sex-workers. She was recognized for her work in 2018 when she was given a special prize for an Outstanding Female Scientist. Ramjee died in March 2020 during another pandemic, COVID-19.

Gita Ramjee (1956–2020)

June Almeida

Finally, the story of June Almeida, a virologist from Glasgow, Scotland. Almeida was born in 1930 and as a child dreamed of going to university to study science. However, as her father was a bus driver the family did not have enough money to send her to university. Instead, at the age of sixteen she left school and went to work in a laboratory at the Glasgow Royal Infirmary (hospital). She later moved to Canada and began working at the Ontario Cancer Institute in Toronto.

At the institute, Almeida worked using a very strong microscope called an electron microscope to study viruses. There she developed a special technique to **identify** viruses which were extremely difficult to see, even under a microscope.

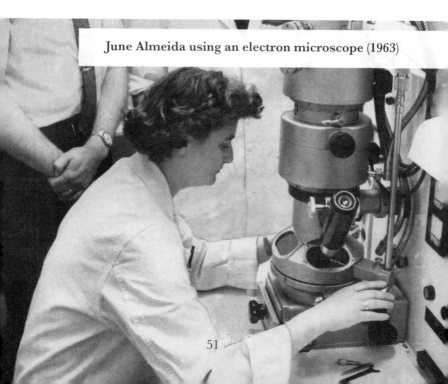

June Almeida using an electron microscope (1963)

Although scientists had studied the rubella virus for many years, before this new technique was introduced no one had actually seen it. Almeida discovered that by putting antibodies under the microscope together with the rubella virus, it finally became possible for scientists to see this virus, as well as others.

In 1964, Almeida returned to the UK and began working at St Thomas's Hospital Medical School in London. During this time Dr David Tyrrell from the Common Cold Unit, who had read papers Almeida had written, asked for her help. He wanted to try to identify a new type of virus that he called B814. With her special technique, Almeida was able to see B814 under the microscope for the first time. She had identified a new type of virus, the coronavirus.

Almeida died in 2007. But before her death she had returned to work at St Thomas's Hospital where she helped produce pictures of HIV. Although she was never recognized for her work in the same way as Barré-Sinoussi and Ramjee, Almeida's techniques for seeing viruses are still used in laboratories today.

CHAPTER SIX

Pandemics in history

In the past, there have been several large outbreaks of disease around the world that we call pandemics. Although many of the pandemics we know about were caused by bacteria and not viruses, the way they affected people in different towns, cities and countries across the world is very similar. Before the 21st century, historians used church documents and diaries to try and understand how pandemics spread. They also learned what people believed about diseases, what they tried to do to stop them spreading and how they tried to cure them. Sadly, the results were not always very detailed or correct. However, using DNA and new research techniques, we can now build a clearer picture of what actually happened to people during these times, how and why they died and why some became immune.

The bubonic plague (Black Death)

The bubonic plague hit the world several times, starting with the Justinian Plague, in around 541 CE, which probably killed tens of millions of people across France, Spain, Germany and the UK. Eight hundred years later, in the middle of the 14th century, the bubonic plague returned to Europe. Researchers believe the bacteria entered Europe on ships carrying goods for

trade, before spreading to the Middle East and North Africa.

The cause of the plague was a bacteria called *Yersinia pestis* carried by **fleas** that lived on rats. After getting bitten by an infected flea the patient immediately caught the plague. Their symptoms, which included large swollen areas of the neck, the size of an egg, under the arm or on the top of the leg, appeared after just a few days. Other symptoms were vomiting, diarrhoea, a swollen tongue and headaches. In the end, the patient's skin turned black and soon after they died. This is how it got the name "the Black Death".

Although the reason why these diseases spread so quickly is simple for us to understand today, at that time, people understood very little about their health. They understood even less about disease. Some believed there was a connection between plagues like the Black Death and the planets. Many thought the plague was started by God to punish the population. The result was that they often turned to religion and the church for help. Groups of men called flagellants travelled from town to town, stood in the market places and beat themselves in front of everyone. They believed that by punishing themselves in this way, they could ask God to forgive them for the disease.

During the 17th century, there were many more examples of the bubonic plague across Europe. The south of Europe saw the worst cases as well as the highest number of deaths, between 30% and 35% of the population in northern Italy. According to research in 2013, the disease was probably the cause of the fall in the **economy** in Italy which became poorer compared to the north of Europe.

Great Plague of London

The Great Plague of London took place between 1665 and 1666. In eighteen months, the Great Plague had killed around a quarter of the population of London; that's around 100,000 people. Many believe it was the Great Fire of London in 1666 that finally stopped the pandemic, by killing the plague rats that carried the disease. However, more recent research suggests this may not be the reason; fewer people were catching the plague by the time of the Great Fire.

The *Yersinia pestis* bacteria that caused the plague was not discovered until 1894 and so people believed you could catch it through the air. The rubbish in the city meant the air in London smelled extremely bad and so, to stop the "bad air", people burned anything: tobacco, even old shoes. Others carried oranges or flowers in front of their noses to hide the smell.

There was no cure for the plague. However, this did not stop people from selling different types of "medicine" to treat the symptoms, including a special kind of tea, cow urine and "plague water". To prevent the disease, they tried killing cats and dogs, but this did not stop the plague from spreading. Instead it brought more rats.

When people became infected, a red cross was painted on their door to show the house was under **quarantine**. However, as the plague continued, not everybody agreed to stay in quarantine. This meant the disease spread even more quickly across the capital. While richer families, as well as the royal family, were able to leave London and the big cities to try to escape the disease, most people could not afford to do this.

The Village of Eyam

One of the saddest and yet most interesting stories of this pandemic is the story of the village of Eyam (around 260 km from London), where the people gave up their lives to prevent the disease spreading to other villages. The plague arrived in Eyam in a box from London containing material to make clothes. Sadly, the box also contained infected fleas and the disease soon spread. While many across England were leaving their towns and cities to escape the plague, William Mompesson, a church leader, persuaded the people of Eyam to stay. If they stayed at home, he told them, they could prevent the disease spreading to other villages and then save lives. So, Eyam was closed, and everyone went into quarantine.

Researchers in 2016 re-examined the story of Eyam. Their research found that the plague had not spread through the air as they had first thought, but person to person. It also proved that Mompesson had been right: although 37% of the population of Eyam died, quarantine did stop the plague spreading to other villages. Keeping things clean, control of rats and the introduction of quarantine proved the best ways to prevent the spread of the plague.

Spanish flu

Unlike the bubonic plague, the Spanish flu was spread by a virus. This was another big pandemic to hit the world. It infected about 500 million and killed around 2.7% of the world's population, possibly up to fifty million people in total.

The Spanish flu was interesting for many reasons and not

only because of the number of people who died. Today, many influenza viruses begin in Asia. However, in the spring of 1918, the Spanish flu appeared in three different parts of the world – the US, Europe and Asia – at around the same time. People believed American soldiers fighting in the First World War brought the virus to Europe, although it is difficult to know the real truth as few documents that measured the number of deaths were actually produced at the time.

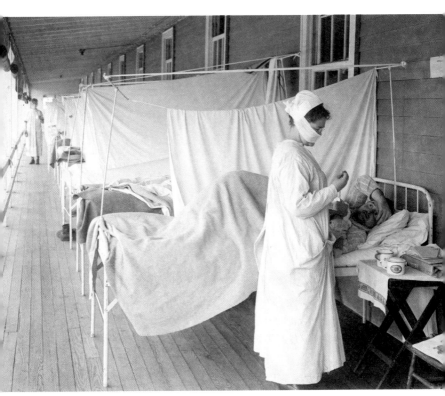

Nurses working during the Spanish flu (1918–1919)

The Spanish flu also appeared more than once. The first outbreak of the virus was in March 1918. It then appeared a second time in September and October and then again in early 1919, first in Australia before then returning to Europe and the US. Having three outbreaks of the same virus in twelve months had not happened before. During the first outbreak, as with other flu viruses, patients suffered from a high temperature, sore throat and a headache. Most experienced these symptoms for a few days, and then got better. Usually a virus is not as bad if it appears a second time, but this was not the case with the Spanish flu. Patients began to suffer from pneumonia, a complication of influenza that affects the lungs. The patient's skin turned blue and their bodies filled with liquid that stopped them from breathing. They died soon after, sometimes within twenty-four hours.

Another big difference between the Spanish flu and other flu viruses was *who* it infected. Influenza usually infects the very old and the very young and people with serious health problems. But for the Spanish flu, the number of deaths was more than twenty times higher for healthy fifteen-to-thirty-four-year-olds than for normal flu viruses. In fact, more US soldiers died from the Spanish flu than died fighting in the First World War.

The third and final interesting fact about this virus was how the Spanish flu infected not only humans but also animals. Research showed that this virus was also transmitted to pigs; not from pigs to humans, but from humans to pigs.

It is possible that the Spanish flu pandemic was started by an army cook in Kansas named Albert Gitchell at the beginning of March 1918. Gitchell reported his symptoms to the army doctor, but by lunchtime that day, more than 100 soldiers in the camp were experiencing the same symptoms. It is believed these same soldiers then helped to spread the disease first across the US and then abroad. James Harris, studying the history of disease and the First World War at Ohio State University, noted that when the war stopped so did the Spanish flu. As it was no longer necessary to send soldiers abroad, the virus stopped spreading.

HIV/AIDS

At the beginning of the 1980s a "new" virus arrived, bringing fear to some populations across the world. HIV/AIDS was soon identified as an epidemic and later as a pandemic. Over the last forty years, international organizations, researchers and pharmaceutical companies have joined the race to find a way of stopping the spread of the virus.

The human immunodeficiency virus (HIV) itself is not new. In fact, it is now believed that the first case appeared in Kinshasa in the Democratic Republic of Congo in 1920. The virus transferred to humans after meat from a type of monkey was eaten. From there it is thought the virus spread to other countries in Africa through the sex trade and also to Haiti, where many people returned during the 1960s after working in the Congo.

HIV was only identified as a virus in the 1980s when scientists were unsure how many people were infected and how it was transmitted. At first, most reports of acquired immunodeficiency syndrome (AIDS), the final stage of infection from HIV, were among **gay** men, haemophiliacs (people with a blood disease), drug addicts sharing drug equipment and people from Haiti. So, it was believed these were the only populations affected by HIV. However, by 1983 there were reports of children who were born with AIDS and scientists began to better understand the virus.

HIV attacks cells in the immune system that fight infection. It is transmitted mainly either during unprotected sex or by sharing drug equipment. Babies can also catch the virus before or during their birth or through their mother's milk. Symptoms develop two to six weeks after infection, usually with a rash, fever and chills lasting one to two weeks. Then, in later years, patients experience more infections than usual, lose weight and have diarrhoea. If the virus is not treated, then within ten years patients can develop AIDS as well as other health problems: a type of skin cancer or cancer of the immune system.

During the 1980s it was unclear how HIV was transmitted and there was plenty of false information, but also fear. Sadly, gay men across the world experienced an extremely difficult time and, often, they were **socially** rejected. Although countries have since introduced policies to stop this from happening, it still continues in some places.

CHAPTER SEVEN

Pandemics and public health

Public health organizations (government groups) are responsible for the health of the population. They do this by educating people about how to stay healthy and avoid disease, and by showing them the connection between how they live and their general health. They can also help prevent disease with vaccination programmes and by encouraging the whole population to work together to help make the health of the country better.

Explaining public health

In order for public health policies to be a success, first we need to understand why health is different for different groups of people. What affects the health of the population? Health is affected by many **social** matters. These include who we are (if we are male or female, our age, our DNA), where we live, our education, what we do (for example if we smoke, eat healthy foods or exercise), where we work, and how much we earn. A good education will often mean a better job with a higher salary. A higher salary means people can afford a better house and eat healthier food. In some countries, this also means people have the money necessary to pay for medication and hospital treatment. The result of this is that these groups of people will probably live a longer, healthier life.

People with lower salaries often work in jobs that are more dangerous, for example as builders or in factories. They may also live in smaller houses or flats with many people living together in a small space. And they might have to travel long journeys on public buses and trains to get to work. The result is that they spend more time in places where disease can spread quickly and easily. All this can have a very negative **effect**, not only on a person's general health, but also on how long they live.

Disease can have a negative effect on other areas of life, too. The result of the bubonic plague in the 14th century was not only the death of millions of people, but also big changes to the economy. Most deaths were in the busy towns, which meant there were few people left to work in the different trades of the time. We also know that fear of others grew and there were sadly attacks on Jews and foreigners during and immediately after the time of the bubonic plague. During the Spanish flu epidemic of 1918, many companies in the US had to close and there were not enough farmers to work the land. Children were left without parents and people even had to **bury** members of their own families.

There were also positive changes because of disease. In Sweden, for example, there was an interesting change to the economy immediately following the Spanish flu. As large numbers of young men were killed by the virus, women had to work in the factories in many regions. At the same time there were also fewer marriages and the number of births fell.

The plague in Florence, Italy

One of the first examples of a good public health **policy** was during the time of the plague in Italy in the 17th century. When the plague arrived in Florence in 1630, the public health organization introduced several policies to help protect the people of the town. Part of the policy was to help feed the poor by giving them bread, meat, vegetables, rice and cheese for free. And to stop people from meeting in large groups and spreading the disease, schools, shops and bars were closed for forty days. Anyone who broke the law was either sent to prison or had to pay a sum of money. According to reports at the time, these public health policies were a success. One in eight people died in Florence during this outbreak of the plague; a number that was far lower than in other towns in Italy where people had continued to live normal lives.

Policies to prevent the spread of disease

Soon after the Spanish flu arrived in the US in spring 1918, hospitals began to find it more and more difficult to manage the number of new patients. The US had to look at ways to stop the disease spreading further and so different public health policies were introduced across the country. The American Red Cross taught the population that to stop the disease, it was important to wash their hands as often as possible and to cover their nose and mouth with a mask. To reach as many people as possible, the organization even wrote their information documents in eight different languages. In San Francisco, wearing a mask became law and people were made to pay $5 if they didn't cover their face. In New York, shops and companies were told to open and close at different times to stop crowds on the trains. Many other towns closed schools, libraries, theatres and churches to stop people meeting in large groups. Those who were sick were often asked to quarantine. According to documents of the time, these policies helped save large numbers from dying.

Some policies had less success, however. Masks were not popular with everyone and in San Francisco the Anti-Mask League fought against this policy when it was introduced. Many shops and companies, as well as schools and churches, fought to stay open during this time to help save jobs and give people hope. In Philadelphia the public health director, Dr Wilmer Krusen, thought it was more important to continue supporting the war and the army than protect the population. So, he decided to lie about the disease, telling people the large number of deaths in the city was because of normal influenza and not the Spanish flu. He then agreed to have the Liberty Loan Parade, a big party to support the war, for hundreds of thousands of people in the city centre. Just three days later there were 635 deaths and by March 1919, 15,000 people in Philadelphia had sadly lost their lives.

Quarantine was not introduced in the UK, and this probably caused the Spanish flu to continue spreading around the country. Despite knowing that quarantine was the best way to stop the flu, the government decided it was more important to keep the factories open. This way they could continue making equipment for the army during war time.

There are several reasons why public health policies are

difficult to manage. One reason is that new viruses are being discovered all the time. According to Public Health England in 2019 twelve new viruses have been discovered in the UK during the last ten years, including MERS (Middle East respiratory syndrome) and swine flu. Vaccines for these new viruses take a long time to develop and are expensive to produce.

Another reason is international travel. Not only do we travel abroad for work and holidays, much of our trade today is international. We saw how travel and trade helped spread both the bubonic plague and the Spanish flu. Today, the chances of this are greater than ever.

Anti-vaxxers

Another worry for the people responsible for public health are "anti-vaxxers". Anti-vaxxers are people who, for different reasons, don't believe vaccines are a good idea. This might include anti-vaxxer parents who refuse to vaccinate their children. Vaccinations are still one of the best ways to prevent diseases caused by viruses. However, some people disagree, while others refuse them because of their religion. More still refuse to vaccinate or to be vaccinated either because they don't trust the science or because they don't trust the government who introduce the programmes. Sadly, in the past when large numbers have refused to be vaccinated, diseases like measles have appeared again. By 2002, measles had disappeared in the US, but this did not stop 600 new cases being reported in 2014, after parents had refused to vaccinate their children.

Today, anti-vaxxers have a new tool to frighten parents: the internet, where false information spreads extremely fast. A few years ago, *Info Vaccins*, a Facebook group in France, posted several messages from parents who said their children had become seriously ill after being vaccinated. Sadly, many French parents believed what they read and stopped vaccinating their children. French public health organizations decided to go online themselves to try and manage the situation. They sent out messages and met parents online to discuss the importance of vaccination programmes like MMR.

In 1998, Dr Andrew Wakefield in the UK wrote a report about a connection between the MMR vaccine and **autism**. Although the research only included twelve children, parents became afraid and suddenly, the number of children being vaccinated in some areas fell to just 60%. The result was that the number of children developing measles rose. The MMR vaccination programme in the UK was in danger and public health organizations were afraid of an epidemic. Dr Wakefield's results have since been rejected thanks to research in Japan. A study of 30,000 children in Yokohama proved there was no connection between the MMR vaccine and autism. In fact, the number of children with autism continued to rise in the town even after separate measles, mumps and rubella vaccines were introduced.

In some countries, parents no longer have a choice as it has become the law to vaccinate all children. This is now the case in France, where children must have eleven vaccines before they can start school. Included in this list of vaccines are polio, hepatitis B, measles and tetanus. Other countries in Europe like Italy, Poland and Slovenia have since followed France's example.

The role of international organizations

It is not only governments that are responsible for public health matters. International organizations like the WHO and the United Nations Educational, Scientific and Cultural Organization (UNESCO) also play an important part in developing policies.

Every year scientists from the 194 member countries of the WHO look at the different types of influenza virus. It is their job to decide which of these viruses to include in the next flu vaccine. Public health organizations across the world then encourage older people and patients with poor health to become vaccinated against the flu. Every year, this helps stop outbreaks of flu around the world.

Another matter that is important for members of the WHO is stopping the spread of polio. They voted to do this in 1988. At that time there were still 350,000 cases of polio a year in 125 countries around the world. Today, because of good vaccination programmes, cases of polio can be found in just two of those countries, Pakistan and Afghanistan.

While the numbers of polio cases have fallen strongly, the WHO still wants to be sure every child is vaccinated. But this is not always simple in countries where there is war, and poor health services. In many places there are not even enough doctors or nurses to run the vaccination programmes. Poor education as well as differences in **culture** and religion also mean that people either don't understand the reason for vaccination programmes or don't trust them. The situation is extremely difficult to manage.

Unless changes are made, it seems pandemics will continue being an international problem in the years to come. The World Bank believes around $6.7 billion a year was possibly lost between 1997 and 2009 because of outbreaks of viruses transmitted by animals; there were six outbreaks during this time. They also note that paying for better prevention and ways to control these diseases in poorer countries will cost $1.9–3.4 billion a year. The UN is worried about the number of new viruses that are transmitted by animals and insects like mosquitos. International trade and travel increase the possibility of spreading these viruses. However, scientists also believe the numbers of mosquitos and other insects is increasing because of climate change. One example of this is the increase in cases

Teaching girls about polio in Pakistan

of West Nile virus that is transmitted by mosquitos. It was noted in 2015 that cases had increased in the south and east of Europe and they believe it may even spread as far as North Europe in the future.

Learning from the past

Being prepared and learning from past events is extremely important for public health. Taiwan, for example, learned from the SARS and MERS outbreaks in 2003 and 2015. When the COVID-19 virus arrived in 2020, Taiwan began taking the temperature of passengers arriving from other countries at ports and airports. And any passengers coming from infected countries were immediately quarantined. It has been noted that these policies helped keep the numbers of people infected by COVID-19 in Taiwan low at that time.

What is clear is that scientists need to work closely with governments in order to develop policies to fight against these new viruses. International organizations and governments must then work together to protect populations and be sure the world is prepared for any future challenges.

CHAPTER EIGHT

Viruses and language

Languages in general are always changing and it is no different in the medical world. As a new disease appears the name often changes, usually because it is too difficult for people to say or write. Language is also a very useful tool. It can be used to educate, to advertise and to inform. Public health organizations have used the power of language to help make necessary changes to the economy and social life in order to stop outbreaks becoming epidemics and epidemics becoming pandemics.

The origin of "virus"

In many languages across the world, medical words first came from Latin and Greek. This means languages often share the same words for different diseases. The word *virus* is a good example. Although Arabic, Finnish, Greek, Japanese, Russian, Turkish and Vietnamese are all very different types of language they all use a word that sounds, and often even looks, very similar to the word we use in English.

The word *virus* has changed meaning several times. We first see the word used in the late 14th century to mean poison. However, we don't find examples of *virus* used in medical documents and books until 1728. As medical understanding develops, we begin to use the word *virus* a little differently. It now means something that the body produces because of disease, which can also infect other people. The word gets a new meaning in the early 1980s when computers are introduced. By 1983, *virus* is used to describe an IT problem that has infected a computer.

The naming of viruses

Diseases and illnesses are often named after the doctor or scientist who first discovered them, like Chagas disease discovered by the Brazilian doctor, Carlos Chagas. The case of norovirus is a little different; it was named after the town of Norwalk in Ohio where, in 1968, 150 children from one school became extremely ill with vomiting and diarrhoea. Researchers took four years to identify the virus that they called norovirus. The Zika virus was named after the forest in Uganda where it was first identified, the Zika Forest.

It is now known that the Spanish flu probably did not begin in Spain. So how did it get its name? When the Spanish flu began, Spain was one of the only countries in Europe that was not fighting in the First World War. As the rest of Europe and the US wanted to include more positive stories, they were not allowed to report on this new virus in the media. Spain was the only country that wrote about it in its newspapers, so people believed that it had come from Spain and that is why they called it the Spanish flu. When the King of Spain, Alfonso XIII, himself caught the virus, this seemed to further prove the story. Meanwhile the Spanish, thinking the virus had entered the country from France, called it the "French flu".

Coronaviruses were first discovered by June Almeida in the 1960s. When looking at the new virus, Almeida noticed that it had a circle around it, and so she named it *corona* meaning *crown* in Latin. The latest coronavirus disease is COVID-19: corona (Co), virus (vi), disease (d), that was first identified in 2019. Before December 2019 the virus *corona* was only known in the world of medicine and it did not become really famous until 2020. Since then the name of the disease has changed several times. In newspapers it quickly became *corona* or *covid* and since we have seen even shorter names, *rone* and *rona,* used online.

Outbreak, epidemic or pandemic

As soon as a pandemic is announced, public health organizations and governments need to find ways to prevent the virus entering the country. Populations in some US towns in 1918 went into quarantine to escape the Spanish flu, and so did the people of Eyam in the UK during the plague. Putting people in quarantine was another way to stop a virus spreading. But where does the word *quarantine* come from? From 1205 to 1358 the port of Dubrovnik in Croatia was controlled by Venice, Italy. As people arrived at the port from countries already suffering from the plague, they had to wait for thirty days before leaving the ship. At that time quarantine lasted just thirty days, or *trentino* as it was called. This later became *quarantine*; the extra ten days was probably added to be sure people were no longer contagious. Today there are twenty quarantine stations across the US where people with yellow fever, cholera and the plague have to isolate.

Having diagnosed the virus, it is then necessary to consider numbers. How many people have already caught this virus and how many more are likely to catch it? The amount of people who become infected by a disease will decide if it is an *outbreak*, an *epidemic* or a *pandemic*. An *outbreak* can be quite small: an outbreak of norovirus in a hospital for example, or a measles outbreak in a school. *Epi* means something that affects an area where a group of people live. According to the US Centers for Disease Control and Prevention, it becomes an *epidemic* when there are more deaths than usual in one area or amongst a group of people. Sometimes *outbreak* and *epidemic* mean the same thing, but people often prefer *outbreak* as they find the word *epidemic* quite frightening. The Greek word *pan* means *all* and the WHO decides an *epidemic* has become a *pandemic* when a virus starts to infect people across many or all countries. The word *pandemic* also brings fear and so it is not a word that is used often. In fact, although COVID-19 had first been identified in December 2019, the WHO did not announce that it was a *pandemic* until 11th March 2020.

Talking about viruses

In the past, we didn't know enough about disease to describe it correctly, so instead we compared it to other things. In the 17th century, to prevent diseases from spreading, you "avoided someone like the plague". This is something we still say a lot in English today when we really don't want to see someone. Many of the verbs, nouns and adjectives we use to talk about disease can be connected to war. A patient might have an "attack of the flu" during the winter months, for example. The media might talk about "The war on SARS" or "Fighting the **battle** against HIV/AIDS". We talk about a norovirus *outbreak* just as we might talk about the *outbreak* of war. We talk about *killing* a virus and *winning* the battle against disease. Health workers sometimes need to *battle* to save a patient's life. Newspapers might write about someone who died "after a long battle with polio".

Today, health workers are advised to use other language to talk about disease. Researchers who study languages believe these words are too negative and unfair and don't help either the patient or the health workers. Comparing disease with a war or a battle suggests the patient didn't fight hard enough to avoid getting ill or that the health workers didn't work hard enough to stop the death of a patient. Instead they prefer to compare disease to a *journey*.

Using language in public health

Public health organizations often use language to encourage the population to take better care of their health. During the Second World War, the UK's Ministry of Health produced posters to remind people that it was important to stay healthy during a time of war. "Coughs and sneezes spread diseases" was probably their most well-known poster. After the National Health Service (NHS) was created in the UK in 1948,

Ministry of Health posters, UK, 1940s

A COVID-19 NHS poster

other posters were produced that used language in a fun way to encourage people to prevent disease. "Catch it, bin it, kill it" reminded people again to stop spreading cold viruses. While during the COVID-19 pandemic of 2020, we saw posters that read "Stay at Home, Protect the NHS, Save Lives".

It is clear that any information given by public health organizations and governments needs to be correct. People often say they have the flu when they really only have a cold. So even something simple like explaining the cold virus is not the same as a flu virus, is important. In 1916, during an outbreak of polio, 72,000 cats and 8,000 dogs were destroyed in New York because people believed the disease was transmitted by animals. In the 1940s, during the summer months, parents asked their children to touch their toes every morning to check they hadn't caught polio. Ten years later, people even refused to talk on the phone as they believed it was possible to catch polio this way. If public health organizations had given the right information at the right time, these false ideas could have been avoided.

Showing change in society

Finally, language can help us to understand the social changes that happen after an epidemic or pandemic. Before the COVID-19 pandemic, only health workers understood PPE, but today even children as young as five know what it means. And in the working world, although the idea of working from home or "WFH" was not new before the pandemic, very few people actually did work from home. But during the pandemic, many thousands of office workers and teachers used technology to do the work we usually do face to face by computer at home. There are lots of advantages of working from home; some even suggest people work much harder at home than they do in an office. In the future it will be interesting to see if companies encourage or discourage workers to WFH.

CHAPTER NINE

Viruses, diseases and culture

Just as war often appears in art, poetry and film, so too do viruses and disease. Through history, diseases from smallpox to the Spanish flu and HIV/AIDS have been topics for writers and artists, singers and dancers. But, sadly, sometimes these diseases have also been the reason for the deaths of many of these same people.

Theatre

William Shakespeare, probably the most famous theatre writer in the world, was born just a few months before an outbreak of the bubonic plague in 1564. Although he didn't actually write about the plague, Shakespeare often used symptoms of the disease in his writing. King Lear describes his daughter as "a boil" (a blister-like spot) and "a plague-sore", while in *Coriolanus*, Marcius calls the people of Rome a "herd of boils and plagues".

Literature

We meet disease again a few hundred years later in Virginia Woolf's *Mrs Dalloway*. Woolf's story takes place in 1923 in the years after the Spanish flu. We learn that the main character, Clarissa Dalloway is, like the author of the book, a **survivor** of the Spanish flu. Although, like Shakespeare, Woolf doesn't actually write about the pandemic of 1918, we believe that when Clarissa talks about influenza, she is probably talking about the Spanish flu. In her diary, Virginia Woolf writes about her own experience of the Spanish flu; a disease which seriously affected her heart.

The most well-known book about disease is *La Peste*, or *The Plague*, written by Albert Camus in 1947. Camus's story takes place in Oran, Algeria, during the time of a plague. Just like the people of Eyam, the city decides to go into quarantine to stop the disease from spreading. Just a few years earlier, Camus had seen Nazi soldiers walk into Paris and control the city. The author, who was interested in psychology, noted how war and plagues affected people in a very similar way. In fact, some believe *La Peste* is more about the effects of war and politics on people than about the disease itself.

Film

Viruses and pandemics have always been a popular topic for film makers. Sadly, these films are often either not very real, or include scientific information that is incorrect. *La Peste* was turned into a film in 1992, but unlike Camus's book, the film takes place in South America. Just like *The Stand* in 1994, which is similar to a book by the popular writer, Stephen King, some films are about viruses and accidents. While in others, like *Code Name: Trixie* that came out in 1973, viruses are used to attack the enemy during war. It is interesting to note that at the start of the COVID-19 pandemic in 2020, the film people most wanted to see was *Contagion*. This was a film produced in 2011 about the outbreak of an unknown virus. Another unknown virus begins to frighten the population in the 1999 film *Fatal Error*, by Armand Mastroianni. We soon learn however that the unknown virus is not what we think and is in fact a computer virus. In 2017, a film company began producing *The Impossible War*, a film about Jonas Salk, the US scientist who discovered the polio vaccine. It is hoped that finally there will be a film about viruses that is at least true to life.

Art

During the centuries, famous artists around the world have painted pictures of and about viruses. Anti-vaxxers in the 19th century probably enjoyed the picture by British artist James Gillray. The artist showed people in a hospital in London just after they were vaccinated against smallpox. The result was parts of a cow that were painted growing from their arms, heads and bodies. A little later in Japan, Utagawa Yoshikazu painted the story of Tametomo who is said to have pushed a smallpox **demon** off the island of Oshima into the sea. One century later, an artist from the Congo made a wooden statue of a young boy with smallpox to remember the last known case of the disease in Somalia in 1977.

Tametomo pushing the smallpox demon off Oshima, Utagawa Yoshikazu

79

Although the Spanish flu killed millions around the world, the disease was important to very few artists. Instead many preferred to paint pictures about the war that was going on at the same time. Edvard Munch, a Norwegian artist who was famous for painting *The Scream*, did however paint pictures about the disease. He painted *Self-portrait with the Spanish flu* in 1919. Munch survived the disease, and later painted a second work which he called *Self-portrait after the Spanish flu*.

Another artist to tell the story of the Spanish flu through art was the Austrian artist, Egon Schiele. In March 1918, Schiele had just had his first successful art show and was becoming famous as an artist. Schiele painted the face of his friend, the artist Gustav Klimt, as he lay dying, some say from Spanish flu. He also painted the face of his pregnant wife, Edith, who sadly died the very next day. Schiele's own life was shortened by the Spanish flu, and he died at the age of twenty-eight in October 1918 before he could finish his final painting, a family portrait.

Frida Kahlo was an artist born in Mexico City in 1907. Her life was full of trouble and she suffered greatly, dying at just forty-seven years old. At the age of six, Kahlo caught polio. The result of the disease was that one of her legs grew shorter and thinner than the other. She hated her legs, preferring to cover them up by wearing long skirts. She developed an interest in art and medicine and at first wanted to draw art books for students of medicine. She became known for self-portraits which were often very dark, showing some of the more difficult parts of her life. Kahlo died of a complication of the lung which was possibly connected to polio.

Keith Haring's art is easy to recognize and can be seen in many of the best art museums in the world. A street artist working in New York, Haring liked bright colours and simple subjects and wanted his art to be for everyone. So, Haring painted about love and about war. He painted in subways and on school buildings. Instead of showing his pictures in art museums, Haring showed them in bars. He also opened a shop that sold his art on T-shirts and posters. He was one of the few artists that could really reach the general public with his art. Haring became known in the 1980s for his pictures about the AIDS epidemic. The artist tried to inform the public about the disease and it proved a success. He died young, at thirty-one, in 1990 because of an illness connected to AIDS.

Another artist who died from HIV/AIDS was Robert Mapplethorpe. Mapplethorpe was most well-known for taking black and white photographs of parts of the body. However, he also took photographs of flowers and objects as well as famous people from the worlds of art and pop music. The work of the American photographer continues to live today through his photographs and through The Robert Mapplethorpe Foundation that gives money for HIV/AIDS research.

Music

In the world of music, there are many reports of 19th and 20th century composers – people who write music – who became infected with diseases like syphilis (Schubert, Schumann and Smetana) and tuberculosis (Chopin). The Russian composer, Igor Stravinsky, caught and survived both the Spanish flu and tuberculosis and was even writing music in his eighties. A problem with his heart caused his death in 1971 in New York.

Pop music has always been known for problems with drugs and there have been a lot of deaths connected to these. Since the 1980s, HIV/AIDS has also been connected to the deaths of many very well-known singers. Freddie Mercury, singer with the band Queen, was famous worldwide in the 1970s and 80s and sold around 300 million records. Just one day before his death in 1991 he announced to the public he had tested HIV positive and had AIDS.

Nigerian singer, Fela Kuti, studied music in London and played saxophone and piano in bars before introducing the world to Afrobeat in the late 1960s. Afrobeat was a type of music that mixed African Yoruba music with different types

Fela Kuti

of popular music. Fela, as he was known, became interested in politics and this affected his music as well as the way he thought. Fela died in 1997 because of an illness connected to the AIDS virus, but only after he had produced over fifty records.

Dance

Finally, to the world of dance. Unlike other types of art, it is impossible to hide behind a virus like HIV/AIDS in dance. We can watch as the virus changes the dancer's body and it slowly becomes weaker and weaker, until finally they are too weak to dance. In ballet, HIV/AIDS has appeared many times since the first outbreak of the disease. In 1989 in *D-Man in the Waters* by Bill T. Jones, the dancer Demian Acquavella, although sick from AIDS and unable to walk, is carried on to the stage to dance using just his arms. It created a sad but beautiful moment.

Dance can be important in the lives of people living with HIV. In Philadelphia, dancers from the Pennsylvania Ballet company helped HIV patients and people with drug problems experience dance. Every week, patients took a ballet lesson where they learned how to use their bodies and to exercise using dance moves. After their lesson, the patients could watch the company dancers as they prepared for their next show.

Many art forms are used to collect money for research into virus treatment and to find a possible cure, including dance. Every year since the 1990s, all kinds of American dance groups have taken part in the Fire Island Dance Festival. Money that is made during the event is given to HIV/AIDS research.

Pennsylvania Ballet company

CHAPTER TEN

Virus survivors and success stories

Disease sadly brings death. Sometimes hundreds of deaths, sometimes millions. However, while there are obviously many sad stories around the topic of viruses, there are also stories of people who survive. Some are famous and others not so famous. Some continue to make a great success of their lives and some have even lived through more than one pandemic.

Survivors

Some of the most famous leaders in history have been attacked by one or more serious viruses. Queen Elizabeth I of England was just twenty-nine when she caught smallpox, which left her without any hair and with small holes in her face that she spent the rest of her life trying to hide. A popular queen, Elizabeth ruled the country for forty-four years despite her illness and died at the age of sixty-nine, which was considered very old at the time.

The Spanish flu affected several leaders during the First World War. The UK's **Prime Minister**, David Lloyd George, almost died from the virus. However, the news was hidden from the British public as it was felt it was more important to stay positive during a time of war. Meanwhile in Germany, Kaiser

Wilhelm II also caught and survived the killer virus. And in Ethiopia, Haile Selassie I, the future leader, became ill and survived. This was at a time when there was a very poor health service in the capital, Addis Ababa, where he lived. Towards the end of the war, US President Woodrow Wilson became so ill doctors thought he was poisoned. He survived and was able to join the discussion with other leaders that finally ended the war.

Winston Churchill, who later became Prime Minister and led the UK during the Second World War, also became ill with the Spanish flu. Sadly, his daughter died from the disease, but his wife, Clementine Churchill, survived. Clementine Churchill worked as her husband's advisor and also became Chairman of the Red Cross Aid to Russia fund during the Second World War, helping to collect £8 million to help Russian people during the war.

José Ameal Peña, or "Pepe" to his friends, was 105 in 2020 and is probably the oldest person in Spain to survive the Spanish flu. At four years old, Pepe was the only one of his seven brothers and sisters to catch the virus. It was difficult at the time to get good medical care in Spain and there was little medication to treat the disease. Churches were not allowed to ring their bells, and the church in Luarca where Pepe lived closed its doors as people believed that there were already so many buried there it could cause a new epidemic. About a quarter of the population of Luarca died from the flu but Pepe and the rest of his family survived.

Pepe has experienced other interesting events during his long life. At the end of the Spanish Civil War (a war between different groups in Spain), he was put in prison by General Franco. According to his family, Pepe escaped by giving his watch to one of the soldiers in the prison. He then walked twenty miles back home to his wife in Madrid.

The March of Dimes

US President Franklin Roosevelt survived polio after catching it, not as a child, but at the age of thirty-nine. In 1938 he started the National Foundation for Infantile Paralysis to fight against polio. The money collected by the Foundation during the Birthday Balls – special parties to celebrate the President's birthday – was given to researchers to help find a vaccine for the disease.

In 1938 the famous radio actor Eddie Cantor started working with big film companies, like Warner Brothers and Metro-Goldwyn-Mayer, to produce a special radio show called "The March of Dimes". The show encouraged the US public to give a dime – a small coin worth one tenth of a US dollar, or ten cents – to the Foundation. Cantor said, "It will allow all persons, even the children, to show our President that they are with him in this battle against the disease. Nearly everyone can send in a dime or several dimes." Cantor was right and after the first radio show the White House got $268,000 (around $4.7 million in today's money).

From then on, the National Foundation for Infantile Paralysis was called the "March of Dimes" and the radio show continued for many years. Over the years, Cantor encouraged other famous people to join him on the show. These included singers like

Frank Sinatra, Bing Crosby and Elvis, actors Marilyn Monroe and Grace Kelly, as well as Joe DiMaggio, the baseball player. One of the researchers to get money from the March of Dimes was Jonas Salk who used it to test the "Polio Pioneers" with his new vaccine in 1954.

The work of the March of Dimes continues today and there are over three million people across the US working for free collecting money for several other diseases as well as polio. More recently, in 2016, President Obama agreed the US government should give $1.1 billion to inform people about the Zika virus and a possible epidemic. Mosquitos carry the virus, but it is also possible to catch it through sex with an infected person. Most infected people will either have no symptoms or very mild symptoms that last between two and seven days. These might be a rash, headache, muscle and back pain as well as pain behind the eyes. The Zika virus can affect pregnant women. Their babies are born with very small heads and suffer problems with the brain.

The man with the iron lung

One of the only people still living in an iron lung today is seventy-four-year-old Paul Alexander. The iron lung is a type of ventilator that helps people breathe. Developed in 1928, it was only meant to be used for two weeks to help children get better after polio. In fact, nobody who needed to use an iron lung was expected to live very long.

Paul caught the disease in 1952 at the age of six during the largest outbreak of polio in the US where 21,000 children were

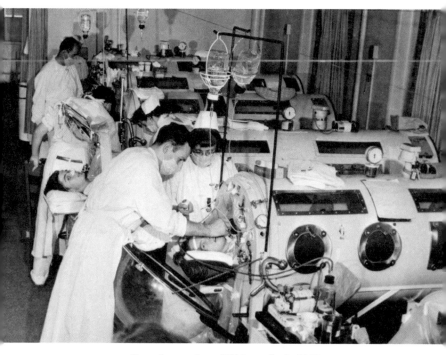

Iron lungs in a US hospital, 1950s

left with some kind of **disability**. At first Paul was treated at home because the hospital near his home was already full and could take no more patients. The little boy was finally taken to hospital where he woke up one morning to find himself inside a machine that made noises. He could neither speak nor move. He couldn't even cough. He believed he was dead.

Eighteen months later Paul was taken home where he lived in the iron lung for three years. After this time, he was able to leave the lung for a few hours every day. Paul's mother taught him to read and he graduated from school at the age of twenty-one before studying to become a lawyer at the University of Texas in Austin. He then worked for several years as a lawyer, living in a special wheelchair that helped to keep his body straight.

Paul writes and can call people on the phone using a special stick like the one his father made for him when he was young. His body has never really grown and is about the size of a child. He suffers from pain in his legs when he is moved and he often has serious problems breathing. As he is no longer able to live outside of the iron lung, Paul now lives in Clements Hospital in Dallas. Paul had survived polio but had not expected to have to live through another virus pandemic, COVID-19.

HIV/AIDS

In 2017 there were 1.8 million new HIV infections, which is nearly half the number in 1996 when there was the greatest number of new infections. This has mainly been the result of good public health policies across the world that have educated people about the virus and how to avoid it. Although the situation has got better, HIV/AIDS continues to be a serious health problem in some parts of the world. This includes countries in the WHO Africa region which has over two thirds of the world's HIV infections. There is no cure, but antiretroviral therapy (ART) protects the immune system by stopping the virus from developing further. Because of ART, HIV patients can now live much longer before developing AIDS. But although 19.5 million people now take ART, in some areas of the world it is still not possible to get it. The UN wants to stop HIV/AIDS spreading by 2030. In order to do this, we need to increase education about the virus and find more ways to prevent, test and treat it.

Ebola

Women are often thought to be very important in fighting the spread of disease. The WHO and UN Women as well as governments in Africa agree that women are the key to success in managing Ebola. In the Democratic Republic of Congo (DRC) where Ebola has returned several times, the WHO, together with the Ministry of Health, have introduced new policies. They have organized places, sometimes hotels, where women with Ebola and their families can quarantine if they wish. During the twenty-one days of quarantine the people are looked after, there are toys and TV for the children, and they are given several medical checks a day. The women learn about the disease and how to prevent it. When they leave, they can then help others to better understand the disease.

A report about Ebola by UN Women asked governments to educate people more about the disease and how to prevent it. The report encourages more women to lead groups to help other women learn about the disease. This might be teaching them how to prepare and keep food safely, or how the disease is transmitted, for example, when feeding their baby. Finally, in areas where Ebola has destroyed the economy, the report suggests women should be encouraged to develop their skills to help rebuild it.

Looking to the future

In 2016, the UN introduced goals for the future of the world: the Sustainable Development Goals (SDGs). Goal 3.3 wants to be sure that by 2030, there will no longer be epidemics of the types of viruses found in this book. Since the introduction of the SDGs there have already been some positive changes. Although it still hasn't reached its final goal, the use of the second measles vaccination, for example, is up to 67%. And in 2019, following an increase in prevention, testing and treatment programmes, adult HIV infections in sub-Saharan Africa had fallen by 37%.

While we are still unsure about the full effect of COVID-19, what is clear is that governments, international organizations, researchers, pharmaceutical companies and medical professionals must work together in order to create a healthier, safer world. That said, with other viruses like influenza continuing to kill between 300,000 and 500,000 people a year, and a new type of flu transmitted to humans from pigs discovered in 2020, there is clearly still much more that can be done to make the health of the world's population better.

During-reading questions

CHAPTER ONE

1 Name two different parts of a virus.
2 Name three ways viruses can be transmitted.
3 What is the difference between an incubation period and a contagious period?

CHAPTER TWO

1 What are the three types of flu virus?
2 How are the rashes for measles, chickenpox and German measles different?
3 What is shingles?

CHAPTER THREE

1 Why is norovirus so contagious?
2 What serious effects can polio have on some children?
3 What is the origin of the Ebola virus?

CHAPTER FOUR

1 What do we know about using honey to treat the common cold?
2 How can you help prevent the spread of a virus when you visit someone in hospital?
3 How did Jonas Salk test his polio vaccination to be sure it was safe?

CHAPTER FIVE

1. What is the job of an epidemiologist?
2. How did Françoise Barré-Sinoussi help other scientists understand AIDS?
3. How did June Almeida help other scientists understand viruses?

CHAPTER SIX

1. Why is the bubonic plague also called the Black Death?
2. How did the people of Eyam stop the spread of the Black Death?
3. What three things were unusual about the Spanish flu?

CHAPTER SEVEN

1. List three things that affect the health of a population.
2. List three policies that were introduced in the US to stop the spread of the Spanish flu.
3. Who are the anti-vaxxers?

CHAPTER EIGHT

1. How did Chagas disease and the Zika virus get their names?
2. What is the difference between an outbreak, an epidemic and a pandemic?
3. What do you know about WFH?

1 What was Shakespeare's connection to the plague?
2 What did the artists Egon Schiele and Edvard Munch have in common?
3 How did the Pennsylvania Ballet company help HIV/AIDS patients?

1 What was the connection between the Spanish flu and some political leaders?
2 How did the March of Dimes get its name?
3 How are women important in the prevention of Ebola?

After-reading questions

1 Look at your answers to the "Before-reading questions". Were you right?
2 What did you learn about the common cold that you didn't know before?
3 How do hospitals try to prevent the spread of viruses?
4 Why is it important for public health organizations to give the right information about viruses?
5 How can antibiotics, antiviral drugs and vaccines be used to treat diseases?
6 What is the role of the World Health Organization (WHO) in preventing the spread of viruses?

Exercises

1 **Write the correct word in your notebook.**

1 oantgeph ....*pathogen*........ a microbe that causes infection

2 itmuoqos .... an insect that carries malaria

3 nmrsitta .... to pass a virus from one person to another

4 elsbtri .... when a spot becomes filled with pus

5 lenpilrkia .... medication that stops us feeling pain

6 bicaonnitu .... the time when the patient has the virus but before the symptoms appear

7 molaptioncci .... when a second medical problem appears

8 zuilennaf .... a very common virus

CHAPTER THREE

2 **Are these sentences *true* or *false*? Write the correct answers in your notebook.**

1 Norovirus was named after the scientist who discovered it. ....*false*..........

2 The advice for norovirus is to stay at home, rest and drink lots of water.

3 The smallpox virus was destroyed in 1967.

4 Every child who catches polio will lose the use of their legs.

5 Ebola can be transmitted from animals to humans through bushmeat.

6 The first outbreak of SARS took place in a laboratory.

3 **Complete these sentences in your notebook, using the words from the box.**

> isolation   antibodies   epidemiologists   antibiotics
> virologists   antiviral   antiviral

1 An ....*antiviral*........ drug is a medicine that stops the virus from developing in the body.

2 Unlike .... used to treat bacterial infections, ... drugs can only be used to treat one kind of virus.

3 In the UK, patients who catch norovirus or MRSA are immediately moved to a room by themselves with their own bathroom to protect other patients. We call this ....

4 .... are researchers whose main job is to study the science behind viruses. They are interested in knowing how different viruses behave and develop.

5 .... look at how and where outbreaks of a disease first begin and how they spread.

6 Almeida discovered that, by putting .... under the microscope together with the rubella virus, it finally became possible for scientists to see this virus, as well as others.

CHAPTER SIX

4 **Write questions for these answers in your notebook.**

1 *How do historians find out about pandemics in history?*
Historians now use DNA to help us understand pandemics in history, but before that they used information found in diaries and church documents.

2 People caught the plague after getting bitten by infected fleas.

3 They drank a special kind of tea, cow urine or "plague water".

4 One of the main differences was that it affected healthy young people.

5 Because the First World War ended and it was no longer necessary for soldiers to travel abroad to fight.

6 They can catch it either before birth, during the birth or through the mother's milk.

CHAPTER SEVEN

5 **Complete these sentences with the correct preposition in your notebook.**

on   from   against   with   by   for   to   of   of

1 Responsible ....*for*............ the health of the population, public health organizations have an important role in preventing the spread ....*of*............ disease.

2 Diseases have many negative effects .... our lives, not just our health.

3 In many regions in Sweden, women had to work in the factories because large numbers of young men had been killed .... the Spanish flu.

4 According .... government documents, policies introduced in San Francisco helped stop thousands .... dying.

5 Wearing masks was often unpopular .... people, and the Anti-Mask League fought .... the policy when it was introduced in San Francisco.

6 After Dr Wakefield's report was written, the public health organization in the UK became afraid .... a measles epidemic.

CHAPTER EIGHT

6 **Complete these sentences with the correct word in your notebook.**

1 Language can be used to help make necessary changes to the *economy* / **economics** during a pandemic.

2 The word virus is also used to describe something that **infects** / **infection** a computer.

3 It took **research** / **researchers** four years to identify the norovirus.

4 They now **advise** / **advice** health workers to use more positive language to talk about disease.

5 Public health **organizers** / **organizations** like the NHS use special language to encourage people to look after their health.

6 By looking at language we can see what **social** / **socially** changes have happened after a pandemic.

CHAPTER NINE

7 Put the words in the correct order to make sentences in your notebook.

1 her own experience of / her heart. / the Spanish flu; / which seriously affected / Virginia Woolf writes about / a disease / n her diary,

In her diary, Virginia Woolf writes about her own experience of the Spanish flu; a disease which seriously affected her heart.

2 the disease itself. / on people / some believe / the effects of war and politics / In fact, / than about / *La Peste* is more about

3 vaccinated against smallpox. / just after they were / people in a hospital / The artist showed / in London

4 the disease was important to / Although / the Spanish flu killed millions / very few artists. / around the world,

5 art and medicine / an interest in / and at first / She developed / for students of medicine. / wanted to draw art books

6 the American photographer / that gives money / continues to live today / through his photographs and / for HIV/AIDS research. / The work of / through The Robert Mapplethorpe Foundation,

8 **Complete these sentences with the correct form of the verb in your notebook.**

1 Some of the most famous leaders in history ....*have been*...... (**be**) attacked by one or more serious viruses.

2 David Lloyd George .... (**catch**) the Spanish flu during the First World War.

3 The money .... (**give**) to researchers .... (**help**) find a vaccine for polio.

4 Paul Alexander .... (**be**) one of the only people still .... (**live**) in an iron lung today.

5 After .... (**survive**) polio, Paul Alexander .... (**not expect**) to experience another pandemic like COVID-19.

6 UN Sustainable Development Goal 3.3 .... (**hope**) there will no longer .... (**be**) epidemics of the types of viruses .... (**find**) in this book by 2030.

Project work

1 Go to pages 109–111. Choose two viruses not written about in this book that you want to read about. Research each virus, looking at the following areas: symptoms, incubation period, contagious period, complications, treatment, prevention, and then write 200 words about each virus, using the information you found.

2 Choose one of the vaccination programmes included in this book. Go online and find out more about it. Make a poster to explain the programme to primary school children.

An answer key for all questions and exercises can be found at
www.penguinreaders.co.uk

Essay questions

1 Choose one of the pandemics included in this book. Explain how the virus began, how it spread, how it was treated, and how it ended. (500 words)

2 Choose a film, book, piece of art or a poem about a virus (it could be one of the examples in this book). Describe how the author or artist shows the virus and discuss why the art was important for the artist or its audience. (500 words)

3 Write about the public health policies for COVID-19 in two countries. How are they the same and/or different. Which one has been more successful, do you think? Give reasons for your answer. (500 words)

Glossary

allergy (n.)
You have an *allergy* when you get red marks on your skin or you have breathing problems caused by something that you have touched or eaten. For example, some people have an *allergy* to cats and dogs, and some people have an *allergy* to nuts.

antibody (n.)
Your body makes *antibodies* when the white blood *cells* notice that a virus has entered it. The *antibodies* fight the virus.

autism (n.)
Someone who has *autism* sees the world differently from most people. They have problems understanding how other people behave, and they often do not like a lot of noise or bright lights around them.

bacteria (n.)
very small microbes (= the smallest kind of life) that live all around us and in our bodies. Some *bacteria* are dangerous. They can make us very ill.

bat (n.)
a small animal like a mouse with wings. *Bats* fly at night.

battle (n.)
a fight between two armies in a war

bury (v.)
to put a dead body under the ground

cancer (n.)
a serious illness that makes *cells* grow in the body in a way that is not normal. *Cancer* can be treated, but it can return and many people die of it.

cell (n.)
the smallest part that all plants and animals are made of

childhood (n.)
the time in your life when you are a child. We usually catch *childhood* diseases when we are young.

common (adj.)
Something that is *common* is experienced by most people.

complication (n.)
something that goes wrong in your body because of a disease or treatment

contagious (adj.)
If you are *contagious* with a particular disease, people can catch it from you.

culture (n.)
music, books and art

cure (n.)
a medicine that stops a disease and makes you healthy again

dehydrated (adj.);
dehydration (n.)
You are *dehydrated* when you do not have enough water in your body and you become weak. This is called *dehydration*.

demon (n.)
in stories, a very bad person who can use magic

diabetes (n.)
There are two types of *diabetes*. Type 1 *diabetes* – when your body does not produce insulin (= something that lowers the amount of sugar in your blood), and type 2 *diabetes* – when your body does not produce enough insulin.

diagnose (v.); **diagnosis** (n.)
A doctor *diagnoses* an illness when they tell you what is wrong with you after asking you questions and examining your body. This is the doctor's *diagnosis*.

disability (n.)
a problem with someone's body or brain that makes it difficult for them to do the normal things that other people can do, like walk or see

DNA (n.)
DNA is in the *cells* of all living things. It tells us what each person, animal or plant is like.

drug (n.)
a chemical that is used as a medicine

economy (n.)
the way that a country makes its money, for example, by buying and selling things

effect (n.)
a change that happens because of another thing

epidemic (n.)
a situation where a *contagious* disease moves very quickly from person to person and a lot of people catch it. An *epidemic* is usually larger than an *outbreak*, but smaller than a *pandemic*.

equipment (n.)
the tools that you need to do a particular job

fever (n.)
If you have a *fever*, you feel ill and your body becomes very hot or very cold.

flea (n.)
a very small insect that jumps. *Fleas* live on animals' bodies and bite them.

gay (adj.)
A *gay* man has sex with other men.
A *gay* woman has sex with other
women.

government (n.)
a group of important people who
decide what must happen in a
country

human (adj.)
human things belong to, or are
connected with, people

identify (v.)
to recognise something and be able
to say what it is

immune (adj.); **immunity** (n.)
If you are *immune* to a disease,
you cannot catch it. This is called
immunity.

immune system (n.)
the way your body works to protect
you from disease

infect (v.); **infection** (n.)
If you are *infected* by a disease, you
catch it. If you *infect* someone, you
give it to them. *Infection* is when this
happens. An *infection* is an illness.

laboratory (n.)
a room where scientists do
experiments

liquid (n.)
something like water

medical (adj.)
connected with disease, medicine,
doctors and hospitals

medication (n.)
a *drug* that you take to *cure* a disease

mild (adj.)
not very serious

mosquito (n.)
an insect that bites animals and
people. Some *mosquitos* can give
you a disease called *malaria*.

negative (adj.)
If you are *negative*, you think
about all the bad things that
can happen. If you are *negative*
towards someone or something,
you are against them.

nervous system (n.)
the way your mind and body
are connected. The *nervous system*
causes you to feel pain if you
injure yourself. It also allows you
to move parts of your body when
your brain tells them to move.

organization (n.)
a group of people with the same
purpose, for example, a company
or a charity (= a charity helps poor
people or ill people)

outbreak (n.)
a situation where several people all suddenly catch a particular disease

pandemic (n.)
a disease that affects many people across a whole country or the whole world. A pandemic is larger than an epidemic.

pharmaceutical (adj.)
connected with *drugs* that are used for *medical* purposes

pharmacy (n.); **pharmacist** (n.)
A *pharmacy* is a shop where a *pharmacist* works. The *pharmacist* prepares medicines that a doctor has *prescribed*.

policy (n.)
a set of ideas or plans that the people in a *government* agree on

population (n.)
all the people who live in a country

pregnant (adj.)
A *pregnant* woman has a baby developing inside her body.

prescribe (v.)
If a doctor *prescribes* a particular *drug* for you, they say that you should take it. They write the name of the *drug* on a special piece of paper and then a *pharmacist* prepares it for you.

prime minister (n.)
a very important person who leads a *government*

protein (n.)
chemical material that covers a virus. It protects the virus and also allows it to attach itself to the host *cell*.

quarantine (v. and n.)
To *quarantine* someone means to make them stay in a place where they have no contact with other people so that they cannot *infect* anyone. If you *quarantine*, you do this yourself. *Quarantine* is a situation where someone does this.

research (n.); **researcher** (n.)
Scientists do *research* when they study the world and find out new information. Someone who does this is a *researcher*.

side effect (n.)
something that you might experience when you take a particular *drug*. *Side effects* are usually not very nice. For example, you might feel sick or have a headache.

social (adj.); **socially** (adv.)
Social matters are connected with the things that people do and the way they live together. If someone is *socially* rejected, they are rejected by other people.

spread (v.)
1. When a virus *spreads*, it starts to *infect* many people.
2. When a virus *spread*s through your body, it gradually affects more parts of your body.

suggest (v.)
If a piece of *research suggests* that something is likely or true, the result seems to show that something is likely or true.

survive (v.); **survivor** (n.)
Someone or something that *survives* continues to live after an illness or an accident. This person or thing is a *survivor*.

symptom (n.)
a sign that someone has a disease, like a pain or a cough

technique (n.)
a special way of doing something

trade (n.)
the activity of buying and selling things

transmit (v.)
to *spread* a disease from one person to another

vaccine (n.); **vaccinate** (v.); **vaccination** (n.); **vaccination programme** (n.)
A *vaccine* is something that is put into your body to protect you from catching a particular disease. When someone does this, they *vaccinate* you. The act of giving someone a *vaccine* is called *vaccination*. When a country's *government* arranges for the *population* to be *vaccinated* against a particular disease, this is called a *vaccination programme*.

Viruses and viral diseases

avian influenza: an *influenza* virus that first came from birds

canine parvovirus: a very *infectious* disease that affects dogs but cannot be transferred to humans

Chagas disease (American trypanosomiasis): a disease that is caused by a small insect that drinks people's blood. It can affect the heart and causes problems for the way we eat.

chickenpox (varicella-zoster virus): a *childhood* disease that causes red spots (= round marks) on the skin and a *fever* (common) **cold** (rhinoviruses): a *mild* illness that makes you sneeze and cough

COVID-19 (coronavirus 2019): An illness that causes many *symptoms*, including a cough, a *fever* (= a temperature above 37°C which is above normal body temperature) and a change to your smell or taste. For many people it is not serious, but older people or people with weak *immune systems* can die from it.

cowpox: a disease that affects cows. People can catch it from them. The *cowpox* virus was used to produce the first *vaccine*.

Ebola: a serious disease that may come from bats and makes you lose blood from all parts of your body

German measles (rubella virus): a *childhood* disease that causes red or pink spots (= round marks) on the skin, *fever*, runny nose and red watery eyes

glandular fever: a disease that causes the neck to become large and painful. It makes people very tired and weak.

hantavirus: a disease that people can catch from mice and rats. It causes *fever* and problems with breathing.

hepatitis B: a serious disease that affects the liver (= the part of your body that cleans the blood)

herpes simplex virus-1 (HSV-1) (cold sore): a painful area on your lip that is caused by an *infection*

HIV/AIDS – HIV (Human Immunodeficiency Virus) – AIDS (Acquired Immunodeficiency Syndrome): *HIV* is a virus that can cause *AIDS*. *AIDS* is a serious disease that is spread through sex and blood. It affects the body's *immune system*.

influenza (flu/the flu): a *common* disease that causes a *fever* and makes you very weak and tired

measles: a *childhood* disease that causes red-brown spots (= round marks) on the skin, sore throat, a runny nose and red, watery eyes

MERS (Middle East Respiratory Syndrome): a serious disease that causes people to have problems with breathing.

mumps: a *childhood* disease that causes the neck to become large and painful

norovirus (winter sickness bug): a common disease that causes stomach ache and makes you sick

pneumonia (viral): a serious disease that causes problems with breathing

polio: (*Poliomyelitis*): a serious disease that can affect the muscles so that the patient cannot walk

rabies: a serious disease that people can catch from a dog or other animal that bites them. It affects the *nervous system*.

SARS (Severe Acute Respiratory Syndrome): a serious disease that causes people to have problems with breathing

shingles: a disease that usually affects older adults and is caused by the same virus as chickenpox. It causes areas of red spots (= round marks) on certain parts of the body, for example, the chest or the stomach.

smallpox: a serious disease that causes a *fever* and spots (= round marks) on the skin. People do not get *smallpox* any more because the *smallpox vaccine* stopped it from *spreading*.

Spanish flu: a serious type of *influenza* that started to spread in 1918. It killed about five million people in the world. It stopped *spreading* in 1920.

tetanus: a serious disease that causes difficulty in moving the mouth and neck. You can catch it if you cut yourself on a dirty, old piece of metal, for example.

tobacco mosaic virus (TMV): a virus that *infects* the leaves of the plant that is used to make cigarettes

tonsillitis (viral): a disease that causes the throat to become *infected* and painful

West Nile virus: a disease that is caused by an *infected mosquito*. Most people do not experience any *symptoms*, but it can sometimes be very serious, affecting the brain and the *nervous system*.

yellow fever: a serious disease that causes a *fever*, bleeding and damages the kidney and liver which turns the patient's skin yellow

Zika virus: a disease that is caused by an *infected mosquito*. It can be dangerous for *pregnant* women because their baby can be born with a small head and problems with the brain.

———————

Bacterial diseases

Black Death: the name of the worst *pandemic* in the history of the world. It caused *bubonic plague*.

bubonic plague (the plague): A disease that killed millions of people in the 14th century in Europe, north Africa and Asia. It caused the area around the neck to swell, painful lumps (= small hard parts) under the skin, and vomiting. Just before they die, the patient's skin turns black.

Justinian Plague: the name of the first *bubonic plague*. It killed millions of people in Europe around 541 CE.

malaria: a disease that is caused by an *infected mosquito*. It has similar *symptoms* to *influenza*, making people very hot and then very cold.

pneumonia (bacterial): a serious disease that causes problems with breathing

syphilis: a serious disease that is *spread* through sex

tuberculosis (TB): a serious disease that makes you cough blood

tonsillitis (bacterial) : a disease that causes the throat to become *infected* and painful

Penguin Readers

Visit **www.penguinreaders.co.uk**
for FREE Penguin Readers resources
and digital and audio versions of this book.